Careers in Sports Science

Simon Rea

CAREERS IN SPORTS SCIENCE

Published in Oxford, United Kingdom 2019

By Adored Publishing

Paperback ISBN 9781916212701

eBook ISBN 9781916212718

Acknowledgements

As this is a self-published book I called upon the time and input of many people and I am so grateful to them for offering it to me generously and in good humour. In particular thank you to the 20 people who agreed to be interviewed for case studies as without you there would have been nothing to write about. I learnt so much from all of you and am excited to pass it on to the next generation.

Thank you also to David Pears, Jenny Stafford-Brown, Sue Hartigan, Alex Twitchen, Simon Penn, Lauren Rose, Steve Ingham, Joe Brittingham and Paul Weighton who provided expert content in areas where I had limited knowledge.

Thank you to William Ellison, Jenny Stafford-Brown for the diligent editing and proof reading that you freely gave of your time to do.

Thank you to Athena Nicolaou for the wonderful, creative cover design that you came up with and for your patience dealing with my numerous amendments

Thank you to my wife, Tanya, for the constant proof reading and valuable suggestions that you made along the way. I don't think that living with an author as they go through intense periods focusing on their writing and generally being uncommunicative is something I would recommend to anyone. It takes a very special person to provide the loving, supportive environment you give me and I am more grateful than you will ever know.

Thank you to my parents, Tony and Pam, for the sacrifices you made to ensure that your children got the best education and start in life they could possibly have. Nothing I have done would have been possible without your generosity and love.

Finally, this book is dedicated to my father-in-law, Colin Stamford (1939-2019), who we lost along the way. The most fun-loving, big-hearted, unique man you could ever meet.

Contents

Chapter 3 - How to give yourself the best chance for a successful career in sport

Chapter 4 – What you need to do to land the job

Introduction

I have been working in the sport and fitness industry for thirty years and in 1986 became one of the first people to study for a degree in the recently established discipline of sports science. When I told people that sports science was the degree I wanted to study most of them reacted with surprise that such a thing actually existed. My father thought I was very lucky to be going to play sport all day, while another friend commented that he had heard about degree courses in basket weaving but that sports science was a new one to him!

Things have moved on considerably since the 1980s and sport and fitness qualifications are hugely popular with over 100,000 students studying sports courses in schools and further education colleges. There are now over 100 universities and colleges offering sports science degree courses producing around 15,000 graduates a year. There has been a significant amount of research produced by sports scientists and many books have been written on disciplines within the subject. Sports scientists are now a common feature of high-performance teams and there are many occupations where sports science degrees are valuable.

In 2015, I wrote a book titled *'Sports Science: a complete introduction'*. After publication I kept getting asked the same question by readers and people I spoke to about the book. It was the same question I was asked when I was studying:

> 'What can you actually do with a sports science qualification?'

When I was studying I would say that I wasn't sure but no doubt I'd find something I'd enjoy. Now I explain that there is a huge variety of occupations you can potentially go into and then give a few examples. This book is an attempt to provide a full and detailed response to this important question.

While my other book started students off on their journey in sports science by providing essential knowledge, this book is about helping students to find somewhere to go. This book arose partly from my own experience, as I had no idea of what I wanted to do with my sports science degree. I knew I liked sport and wanted to work with people but that was the extent of my aspirations. This had a huge impact on my career because it meant that I didn't try to gain any relevance experience or have any basis on which to select the modules I would gain most benefit from studying. It is fair to say that I was a fairly aimless student and with a clearer idea of my goals and future plans I would have made a lot more of my time spent as a student. I eventually discovered a career path that suited me, but I had a lot catching up to do to develop the skills and knowledge I needed.

While I would never suggest that you should know exactly what occupation you want to go into aged 16 or 18 or even later, it is important that you have the information that you need to help you make decisions about which courses you should study when you finish your GCSEs or are leaving school. By having some understanding of what it might be like to work in different sport and fitness roles you can start to consider your options, narrow down your interests and start to make better informed decisions about what you are going to study. If you have a focus to your study it makes it a lot easier to motivate yourself and produce the resilience you need when things get tough.

I decided that rather than present information about job descriptions and entry requirements the best way to do explore careers was to talk to people who are actually doing these jobs and hear their stories. This way I could get an accurate account of the qualifications and experience that you need to work in selected roles and what it is actually like to do that job. I looked at what people working in sport do on a daily basis and the parts of the job they enjoy, and those parts that are less enjoyable. This way a picture was built up about what doing that job is like to give you an idea about whether it is something you would like to do and whether it would suit your personality and skills.

This book is supported by my website where you will find details of my other book, blog posts on careers in sport and other interesting information. My website is at:

simonreasportscience.co.uk

The structure of the book

This book is organised into four chapters and you should focus on the sections that are most relevant to you at any point in time. The chapters will take you from when you are aged 16 and choosing a course to study, right up to the point where you have finished your studies and are applying for jobs.

Chapter 1 – Routes into sports careers - making sound educational choices

Deciding which career you want in the future and how you are going to get there is a complex process. Chapter 1 of this book looks at the different types of courses that you can study post-16 so that you can choose the one that best suits your needs and style of learning. The education landscape is constantly evolving with recent changes to A-levels and BTEC courses, the development of Tech levels and new apprenticeships, so we will look at each type of study and explain what they involve and which types of students they may suit. In particular, there is a focus on whether A-levels or BTEC courses offer the best preparation for degree level study. Chapter 1 also asks the question 'why should you study for a degree?'

This is a fair question when you consider the cost of a degree and time you will spend studying for a degree when you could become a coach or personal trainer by studying a short course that lasts a couple of weeks or months. You have to be sure you are making the right decision. Chapter 1 also looks at how you should go about choosing a university degree course and the factors you need to consider.

If you have already started degree level study then Chapter 1 will have limited relevance for you, so I suggest that you skip to the later chapters. However, the sections on the value of a university degree may help to remind you of why you are studying and keep you focused.

Chapter 2 - Case studies of people working in sport

Chapter 2 presents 20 case studies of careers in sport and fitness as told by the people working in them. Each case study is based on interviews I conducted between 2017 and 2019. The case studies explore the qualifications needed to get into that occupation, the daily roles and responsibilities of each occupation type and what a typical day's work might look like. Unsurprisingly, it appears that typical days don't really exist in most sport and fitness jobs. Each case study also provides advice to students who are interested in that type of work and what they need to do to give themselves the best chances of finding work and standing out from the crowd. This section also explores the personal skills that are required to work effectively in the role. These are also referred to as 'personal', 'employability' or 'craft' skills. They are the important additional skills, such as communication and creativity, that employers are increasingly looking for when selecting people to work in their organisation.

Chapter 3 - How to give yourself the best chance for a successful career in sport

Chapter 3 is probably the most important chapter in the book as here we consider the challenges of working in sports and fitness environments that can be pressurised and fast moving. Working with people who may be athletes, coaches or fitness clients, presents a whole set of challenges and problems to navigate around. This chapter assesses why university study may not always prepare you fully for work in sport and fitness and explores the personal skills that you will require to be effective in these environments. The chapter concludes by presenting ten things that you can do during your studies to give yourself the best preparation for your future career. These ten things are based on content that has come out of the interviews presented in Chapter 2. They represent the key messages that I wanted to convey to undergraduate students to give them the best chance of being effective when you finally stand in front of an athlete, coach or fitness client and have to showcase your knowledge and skills.

Chapter 4 – What you need to do to land the job

Chapter 4 considers the nuts and bolts of getting a job. It may not be the glamorous stuff, but it is vital in enabling you to present the best version of yourself to potential employers. This covers job applications, CVs and covering letters which contribute significantly to you getting the all-important job interview. We will then look at how you should prepare for an interview and covers vital issues, such as 'what questions should I ask?' and 'what should I wear to the interview?' This chapter may not be as relevant to you as the others at this point but it will be once you come to apply for jobs. It is still beneficial for you to look at this process so that you know what you are eventually planning and working towards.

A word of apology

In a book of this length I have not been able to cover as many occupations as I would have liked to, and I am aware that there are some occupations that are not well represented. For example, I have not been able to cover GP referral consultants, cardiac rehabilitation specialists and people working in health promotion which all offer valuable and fulfilling work to sports science graduates. I apologise for this and am also aware that there may be biases in my selection that reflect my own interests and the network of professionals that I interact with. I was very fortunate that some interviewees referred me on to some of their contacts. This has meant that certain organisations and clubs have become overrepresented in my sample and I apologise to those who are not represented.

In Chapter 2 I have presented the experiences and views of the 20 people I interviewed, and these are based on their own knowledge and experiences. They are not intended to be presented as the only way, or even the best way, to get into these occupations. Nor do they represent the experiences of all people who work in these occupations. I hope you will receive the information as it is intended and that is to provide examples of what it is like to work in a selection of sports science related occupations from personal viewpoints

Finally, I have presented this book as being about careers in sports science and what you can do with a degree. It must be pointed out that I have covered some occupations that can be accessed without a degree and indeed some of the people I interviewed do not have degrees or hold degrees in other subjects. This does show that there are multiple ways to access careers where sports science is a valuable subject to study, but it is not always necessary to have a degree to work in it. On the flip side, there are also many non-sports careers that can be accessed if you have gained a sports science degree.

Chapter 1 – Routes into sports careers - making sound educational choices

Introduction

Education choices are becoming increasingly complex as there are a greater range of courses and routes into employment than there has ever been before. It can be difficult for students to assess the options and then make the right choice. This chapter is aimed at students and also parents or anyone who is advising young people so that they are aware of the choices and the implications of choosing a certain route.

In this chapter I will be aiming to answer the following questions:

> Is a degree really worth having?
> How should you choose a degree course?
> Is it best to study A-levels or BTEC style courses after GCSEs?
> What other options are available?

This chapter covers a lot of ground in relation to key information about education but as everyone will be at a different point in their studies of sports science you should pick out the sections that are relevant to you and your current position.

Before we look at the choices in education, I want to explain why it is important to have an idea about what you want to do once you have completed your studies.

Why it is important to be a directed student

It is important that you know about the employment options in sport because your studies will have a major impact on your future and ultimately your happiness and fulfilment. It is likely that you will spend 40 to 50 years of your life working and a job is something that can be enjoyed or endured. You may not always enjoy every part of your work and you may even do some jobs as a stepping stone to more fulfilling work but having an aim or a goal is important because it will inform all the decisions that you make and give you direction for your future actions.

In the short term having some idea about your future will help you to make decisions about whether you would like to go to university, where you would like to go, which modules you should choose to study and what else you should be doing to make the most of your time at university.

The worse thing that you can do while you study is to be what I call an 'aimless student' and I know this because I was once of them. An aimless student is one without any idea about their future direction and what they are interested in. Subsequently they don't have any basis on which to choose the degree they want to study or which modules to select during their studies. Rather than making positive decisions while they study they will choose modules based on criteria such as:

> What are my friends studying?
> When are the lectures held and will it allow me to have a lie in?
> Which modules are left over?

This type of student will study for three years, then panic and dive into the first job that is offered to them, as it will buy them some time before making any big decisions. This is exactly what I did and while I was able to sort myself out, I had a lot of catching up to do and additional work to put in before getting myself onto the right career route. I don't recommend it!

However, I do hear students say, 'how can I know what I want to do aged 18?' and I understand that you can't make decisions if you don't know the options. The case studies in Chapter 2 of this book will help you to make an informed decision and formulate a goal for your career. In my experience having a goal does not necessarily mean that you will achieve it but working positively towards a goal tends to open up other unforeseen options that you weren't previously aware of. Often these options are better than the one that you were working towards. For example, in my mid-30s I decided I wanted to become self-employed to work as a lifestyle coach in the fitness industry to help people stick to their training programmes and achieve their goals. I wanted to do this alongside writing textbooks and the lifestyle coaching would give me the short-term income to allow me to do my writing. At this point I also spent a lot of time talking to people in the sports industry and offers of work came up, some of which I took and some I didn't. However, one contact alerted me to a job that he thought was perfect for me as it offered the chance for me to use my experiences of writing and working in the fitness industry. I successfully applied for this job and that is how I came to work at The Open University and have done so for the last 12 years. This job has offered me the chance to do everything I enjoy doing, such as writing, designing courses and developing audio-visual resources. If I hadn't made that visit on that day I would never have been alerted to that job.

The opposite to an aimless student is a directed student and that is one who is active in the choices that they make and has a basis on which to make every decision so that it is in their favour. I have no statistics to back this up but being an active student is more likely to lead you to where you want to go, and you are likely to get there more quickly. To be an active student is to look at all the options and choices that you have and to talk to as many people as you can about future careers. This may be people who work in those careers, careers advisors, university staff at open days, friends and family.

If there is a single aim of this book it is to help you make decisions about what career path you would like to follow and then become focused and make good decisions that will help you work towards that goal. Thus, avoiding becoming an aimless, directionless student and being one who is directed and motivated.

The value of a university degree

You may not need me to explain the value of a university degree, but as you will be responsible for your tuition fees, which are around £30,000 for a three-year degree plus additional living costs, you may need to justify these costs to yourself.

Firstly, there are many occupations that will require you to be a university graduate to be considered for that role. The list shows some of the careers where a degree is a minimum requirement and some where a degree is not necessarily required.

A sample of graduate and non-graduate careers:

Graduate careers

Exercise physiologist

Sports analyst

Sports nutritionist

Sport psychology

Sport physiotherapist

Teacher/Lecturer

Non-graduate careers

Sports coach

Fitness trainer

Personal trainer

Recreation assistant

Outdoor pursuits instructor

Sports development officer

Having a degree opens up a world of opportunities to you and also takes away limits on how far you can go in your career. It must be said that often a degree is just a first step into graduate careers and to progress you may need higher level qualifications and specific work-related qualifications. For example, to work as a sport psychologist you will need the minimum of a master's degree and also meet specific regulations set down by a professional body before you can practice. You will understand this more when you read the case studies in Chapter 2.

Careers in sports coaching and personal training can be entered either through completing a short course or as a graduate of a degree course. The next section assesses the value of completing a degree over short courses.

Short courses versus university degrees

This is a good question and one that you will need a convincing answer. It is true that you can become a Level 1 coach in football after 43 hours of study including eight workshops, a fitness instructor after two weeks' study and a personal trainer after an additional four weeks' study. These qualifications will give you a licence to practice within certain boundaries.

It seems to make sense that if you want to work in these occupations then you should do these short coaching courses and get started – or does it? I asked three university lecturers about the value of a degree for people who want to become coaches or personal trainers. Firstly I spoke to David Pears, who is a Senior Lecturer in Sports Coaching at the University of Bedfordshire.

What is the value to students in doing a degree rather than going straight into employment?

People generally progress further with a degree so while there is a financial cost you should gain graduate level employment and earn more afterwards. Having a higher level of learning will mean that you understand more about your subject area and be able to answer the 'why' as well as knowing the 'what' and the 'how'. As a practitioner in coaching, sports massage or personal training you will understand the science behind the practice and be able to answer questions and critically evaluate new practices when they come along. For example, high intensity interval training (HIIT) came along a couple of years ago you would be able to answer questions such as 'why does it work?' and 'how does it work?' as well as being able to deliver it safely to your clients.

If you want to become a coach, you can do your coaching courses and become qualified and likewise you can qualify to be a personal trainer in six weeks so what is the benefit of doing a degree in the subject?

If you do a short course there is only a certain amount of time for content to be delivered and understood. You might learn what to do and how to do it as well as the basics of the role, but you won't have a full understanding as to why you are doing you are doing it. Short courses are important to help learn the 'what' and the 'how' and they are often delivered by excellent tutors, but there is a limited time to develop your skills. They serve an important purpose and can lead to work, but your future opportunities will be always limited unless you develop and educate yourself in other ways.

Is it fair to say that someone who has a done a three-year degree and someone who has done a three-week course could end up in the same position?

Yes, because a degree does not automatically get you a higher-level position; it can do but it is not guaranteed. You may come out of university and initially have to get a non-graduate job because you may need some experience if you have not gained any while at university. You should be able to progress more quickly by showing what you can do and then doors will open up for you.

A short course will only get you so far, but you might find that after a couple of years you are ready to move on to other things and the person with the degree may have more options to explore after that.

A good degree will ensure that your eyes are opened to the opportunities available and because you have a greater depth of knowledge you will be confident to move into other roles. Graduates can be more independent and look around for new things to get involved in. Degree level study can broaden your horizons, give you opportunities to network and get involved in things.

David made several important points about the importance of the increased depth of knowledge that graduates will gain with prolonged study and how this can help you to progress further in your career and increase your options. He also stresses that degree level courses develop additional skills such as critical thinking and independence.

I also spoke to Dr. Alex Twitchen, who is a Senior Lecturer in Sports Coaching at the University of Chichester, and he clarified the difference between a degree and a short course in coaching:

What is the difference between completing a short course in coaching and a three-year degree?

A typical governing body coaching qualification will provide students with a good level of technical and tactical knowledge of a particular sport, but it will not provide as detailed an education as a degree course. A governing body coaching qualification should be viewed as a form of training rather than an education.

What is the benefit of studying for a degree?

An undergraduate degree provides a deeper and more intellectually challenging analysis of the theories and concepts that underpin sports performance, how to coach and current issues in sports coaching.

Dr. Twitchen was keen to highlight that degrees don't just teach knowledge but that they also develop transferrable skills which are skills that can be applied in other occupations and increase an individual's employability potential. Graduates in sports related degrees will develop the following transferable skills:

Analyse theories and concepts and apply them to practice.

Collect, analyse and interpret data

Communicate ideas and present findings.

Demonstrate problem-solving skills.

Show well developed interpersonal skills

Reflect on their own practice and have high levels of self-awareness

I asked Simon Penn, Senior Lecturer in Health and Exercise Science at St Mary's University about the value of degree level study for people who want to work in fitness as personal trainers or fitness instructors.

What are the differences in skills and knowledge between people who have studied a short course in fitness instruction or personal training and those who have studied for a degree?

A six-week personal training course provides an individual with the basic template of how to create a general training programme for an individual. However, studying for a degree provides three years of experience spent reading the latest research and critically analysing techniques to identify the optimal methods for each training goal. Therefore, a personal trainer with a degree should provide a more robust and effective training programme.

Students have often asked me why is it good for a personal trainer to have a degree? I tell them to think about a job interview scenario. If you had the choice would you rather hire a personal trainer who has done a six-week course and learnt their trade on the job through watching other people in the gym, or employ a personal trainer who has trained for three years under leading experts and can rationalise why they have selected specific exercise techniques that are based on research?

Finally, I asked Lauren Rose, a graduate of The Open University BSc (Hons) degree in Sport, Fitness and Coaching about the impact that studying for a degree had had on her work as a tennis coach.

How have your degree studies impacted on your tennis coaching?

Completing a degree has had a huge impact on my coaching career. I strongly believe it has made me a better coach in a number of ways. It enhanced my somewhat limited knowledge of nutrition, strength and conditioning and biomechanics. Very little of these subjects are taught on tennis coaching courses or within the CPD we are encouraged to access. I think the area of my studies that has proved most useful to me as a coach is the psychology I studied, and in particular learning about coach-athlete-parent relationships. As a result I have learnt to give my players more autonomy or independence and this has had a big impact on their willingness to train hard, but most importantly allowed them to feel more in control during match play. Unconsciously prior to studying and then implementing this, I was very much in control of every aspect of my players coaching; for example, what we would work on in training and what their targets should be. Aside from the knowledge I gained from the degree itself, it also helped to increase my resilience, perseverance and time management. All of which are key skills for me as a coach and also for me to instil in my players.

In summary it seems that degree level study does equip you with many more skills than studying short courses. It is not only the depth of knowledge that is developed but also an individual's ability to apply their knowledge and be critical about the techniques that they are using. The additional transferrable skills developed during degree level study are beneficial to students who wish to change direction and work in other professional occupations, with teaching being an obvious one. This practice is increasingly common that students use their degree in a generic way and use it as evidence of a certain level of learning.

Choosing your university degree

It is difficult to get completely accurate figures on the number of students studying sports science degrees and the number of courses available but UCAS (2019) say that in 2014/15 there were 43,340 students studying sport related degrees. This fits in with Ingham's (2018) assertion that there are around 15,000 students graduating each year and thus around 45,000 students studying sports science at any one time.

UCAS (2019) show that there are 134 providers of undergraduate courses (universities and colleges) with 476 courses to choose from. While most of these courses are either degrees in sports science or sport and exercise science there are many courses that offer sports science with a secondary focus or specialism. Specialisms can be done in a range of subjects such as:

Physical activity
Health
Performance sport
Coaching
Sports management
Nutrition
Psychology
Personal training

It is worth searching on the UCAS website to assess the range of options for courses that are available. There is also a range of subscription based websites designed to help you chose university courses available, such as Unifrog, which your school or college may be signed up to.

Specialisms are a good choice if you have a clear idea of your interests at this point. If you are not sure then studying a sports science course will help you to experience a range of subjects and you can often specialise in certain areas after the first year of the course.

When you decide to study at university you are making an investment of at the time of writing, around £30k on tuition fees and a similar amount in living costs and at some point you will have to pay this money back. It is important that you make that investment wisely, so you need to plan and do your homework. The first thing that you need to know is that the glossy prospectus that is produced by the university is a marketing tool. It is designed to be attractive and so will present everything in the best light. Many universities also have an online prospectus written by students to give an authentic view point of what the course and university are like from the student's perspective; these are well worth reading to support your decision making process.

You need to look at the content of the course and assess whether it offers the modules that interest you. You can find this content online or at an open day. When choosing a course it is very important to look at whether the course will provide you with practical experience. In particular look for universities that can offer an internship or industrial/work-related experience. These types of experience will improve the skills that employers are looking for. A good degree course will provide excellent learning experiences but also the opportunity to put those skills into practice with real people in real situations.

Other things to assess are whether you will get the academic support that you will need to be successful. While you may get told about academic support at an open day it is important find out what the academic staff are like and you can do this at the open day. When you talk to staff you need to see whether they have time for you and how they engaged with you.

Studying for a degree is about choosing the right course and I believe that should be central to your decision of where you would like to study but there are many other important factors as well. In particular, the environment where you are studying for your degree will impact on your success during your course and your future. You need to visit the campus and find out what the halls of residence, student accommodation, the library and the canteen are like and whether you get a good feeling about them. Obviously when you study sports science it is important to look at the sports and fitness facilities and check that they provide opportunities for your own training, and for competing at your sport

A key question is where you will study and this throws up several more questions, such as would you like to stay close to home or move away? Which are the best universities to study at? Where will I find the lifestyle that I enjoy? It is beyond the scope of this chapter to answer these questions, but I would advise the following:

Check out The Times Good University Guide to find out which are the highest rated universities that provide sports sciences courses;

Find out the university's rating on the Teaching Excellence Framework (TEF) as they will have a rating of gold, silver or bronze depending on the quality of their teaching;

Go to as many open days as you can and check out all the facilities to see that they match your needs and expectations for your sports and social life;

Spend some time in the town or city and see whether you like the environment where you will be living for at least three years.

The three years that you study at university should be three of the best years of your life but only if you are studying the right course for you in a place where you are going to be happy. The choices you make impact significantly on your life and future career so spend time researching courses and visiting universities so that you can make the best choice.

I would advise that you look at league tables for the top courses and TEF ratings but don't use the information as the sole basis for your decision. You will have your own individual academic needs and interests as well and knowing what you need in your environment to enjoy yourself when you are not studying. You should use these to guide you towards your decision as well.

Do A-levels or BTEC courses best prepare students for undergraduate study?

It may be that you have already made your choice of what to study between the ages of 16-18 but if you haven't then the next two sections will be of interest to you. The choices for Further Education (aged 16-18) study are becoming increasingly complex with choices to be made between studying A-levels, BTEC courses, or a mixture of both. There are other options you can choose to get access to sports careers but if you want to study in Higher Education (degree level study) then it is important to assess the options.

To gain entrance to Higher Education you will need to study either A-levels or a Level 3 BTEC course. If you choose the A-level route then you would need three A-levels and there is a broad choice of subjects to choose from. A-levels in science, particularly biology or human biology, will always be useful as will PE, psychology and mathematics. English is useful for the written components of degrees. You will need to check out the individual requirements that universities make when offering a place.

Alternatively, you can study a BTEC-style course and gain access to Higher Education this would need to be a Level 3 course. There are different sizes of BTEC course available, and the main ones are:

Extended diploma – equivalent to 3 A-levels;
Diploma – equivalent to 2 A-levels;
Extended certificate – equivalent to 1 A-level.

The other option is to study a combination of A-levels and BTEC courses; for example, students choose to study a National Diploma (2 A-levels) alongside an A-level to make up three A-level equivalent.

But when deciding there are a number of questions that students, and their parents, will need to consider:

> What is the best route to take?
> What will suit the individual student best?
> Which route will universities look on more favourably?

To answer these questions I spoke to two Chief Examiners, Jenny Stafford-Brown, who is a Chief Examiner for BTEC Level 3 courses and Sue Hartigan, who is a Chief Examiner for GCSEs and A-levels in PE. Firstly, Jenny Stafford-Brown will explain the differences between studying for BTEC courses and studying for A-levels and identify which type of student is best suited to the BTEC style of learning.

Tell me about post-16 BTEC qualifications in sport and sports science

> Within the area of sport there are two qualifications. Firstly, the BTEC Nationals in Sport, which are for learners who are interested in sports development, coaching and outdoor pursuits. The second qualification is BTEC Nationals in Sport and Exercise Science which are designed for students who want to study sport and exercise science at university. They are vocational in nature as they always have some sports sector related application. So whilst learning the underpinning knowledge there will always be links to how that knowledge can be used in practice. This is either through the content of the qualification, or through the assessment process whereby learners are put in a certain context. For example, there may be a scenario where they are working as a sport and exercise scientist and they are asked how they would apply their skills and knowledge to sport and exercise science scenario.

> Vocational qualifications also have the additional benefit of preparing students for university study as there is a focus on independent, student centred learning which they do as part of the coursework element of the qualification. With A-levels there is little emphasis on coursework and the focus is on the endpoint assessment – the exam. BTEC learners do a significant amount of coursework and have to go out and research topics using a variety of resources, such as journals, text books and websites. This prepares them well for university when they have to conduct independent research. Universities have reported that

students who have done a BTEC qualification are much better prepared for this element of a degree.

How would you explain the difference between BTECs and A-levels to a parent?

The key thing is that people often see the vocational route as one that is less academic and that may have been the case in the past. The assessments were based on pass/fail criteria as to whether students were competent or not to complete that particular qualification. Now as applied general qualifications there is much more similarity across BTECs and A-levels and both offer UCAS points linked in similar ways. A distinction* equates to A* at A-level so there is parity across the qualifications in terms of grades. BTECs do support progression to university in the same way that A-levels would.

At A-level students get to choose three or more different subjects meaning they may be choosing some subjects that they don't necessarily like but have chosen it to gain sufficient UCAS points. With BTEC qualifications you can choose different sizes of qualification so there is the option to choose a BTEC that is equivalent to one A-level (Extended Certificate) , one and a half A-levels (Foundation Diploma), two A-levels (Diploma) or three A-levels (Extended Diplomas). This means students can focus their Level 3 study on an area that they have an interest in because they want to go to university. It means they are more likely to be engaged throughout the course than a variety of A-levels where they may not be fully engaged in all of them.

BTECs also offer the ability to do hands on learning as they have different types of assessment as well as coursework to help develop softer or behavioural skills that are needed at university and in future working environments. For example, many centres use presentations which get students used to speaking in public, developing skills to use software for presentations and their ability to speak and present information to an audience. They are unlikely to do this as part of A-level study.

They will also develop their research skills because part of the BTEC qualification requires research. They will learn about different types of research and this helps with progression to university study. These new reformed university qualifications with external assessments and updated content means that often universities are choosing them over A-levels because students are more likely to achieve on their degree courses. In the past universities have asked for an A-level alongside a BTEC qualification for courses such as physiotherapy which are very competitive, but many universities are now accepting BTECs alone in recognition that they are comparable to A-levels.

Is there a certain type of student who is best suited to BTEC style learning over A-level?

I would say yes, because there is much more active learning whereby students go off and find out things for themselves and apply their knowledge. It suits students who are less keen to sit for a long time in the classroom and take knowledge in. Kinaesthetic learning is the term used for students who like to learn through exploration and BTECs provide much more scope in comparison to A-levels, as A-level teaching can favour the talk and chalk approach.

Also learners who have special education needs, such as dyslexia, do well on BTEC courses because there is more coursework, and this can support students who may struggle with external assessments. While there are external assessments on BTECs they are not the main method of assessment as they are on A-levels.

Also BTECs are not performance related, in that students have to know about sport and take part in sport they don't have to be high level performers to do well. A-level PE does have a performance related element whereby your performance is assessed. Some students may be more interested in exercise than sport and this is supported by BTEC qualifications.

If a student wanted to study a BTEC alongside an A-level are there any A-levels that would be a best fit?

It really depends upon what the student would like to study at university. In terms of content, biology A-level is a good one because it complements the strong biology content in BTECs. For students who want to become PE teachers then A-level PE is a good choice, but universities may not recognise both qualifications for admission as they see the content as too similar. A-level psychology is a good choice because it works well with the sport psychology in the BTEC courses. There is also sociology on both BTEC courses so that could be complementary.

A lot of advice now from schools about choosing A-levels is about asking students what they enjoy and like doing as that really helps with commitment and achievement in the classroom.

One added benefit with BTECs, which is something that is being adopted in schools, is getting students to select the 90-credit option (Foundation Diploma) which is equivalent to one and a half A-levels to be studied alongside two A-levels. This gives the bonus of added UCAS points and can support progression to a university that may make a slightly higher offer. The student only has to study a couple of additional units to get the extra UCAS points.

Jenny has explained the benefits of BTEC style study and it particularly suits students who prefer continuous assessment rather than working towards a final exam which is the only assessment that counts. There are up to four external assessments on BTEC Level 3 courses now and while they count towards the final grade they are only a small part of its calculation.

Sue Hartigan is an experienced teacher and examiner of A-level and GCSE P.E and she explains the types of skills that are needed to be successful at A-level, what A-level PE involves and the two routes that can be taken to become a PE teacher.

How would you explain to a parent the difference between studying A-levels and a BTEC course?

There are significant differences between methods of study. BTEC students have to be able to motivate themselves independently to get on with their studies. While this is important in both types of study, it is particularly important in BTEC courses because of the style of delivery where you have to research topics for yourself and continually complete coursework assignments.

Alternately you get some students who are very happy with clear guidance about what they need to learn and know and are very good at recall and using that information and applying it. Those are the types of skills that you need at A-level with a particular emphasis on being able to recall information.

The main thing is which method of studying do you prefer and when are you most successful. Do you enjoy being in a classroom, sitting, learning, taking lots of notes and making sure you can reproduce that kind of learning in an exam situation. If so then A-levels are most suitable but if you prefer independent study and different ways of learning such as group work and being assessed through assignments, then BTECs would be best for you.

There is also a difference in how the courses are assessed as A-levels are assessed by a final exam and BTECs use coursework as a means of continuous assessment. BTEC Nationals have now moved towards demanding more of the same type of skills as A-levels with the introduction of external assessments, although in a much smaller proportion. For a student who wants to achieve a

Distinction in their BTEC they must do well in their external assessments and will therefore need the same types of skills of learning, recalling and applying knowledge as A-level students. This shared element of external assessment makes it more difficult to differentiate between what were previously two distinct groups.

What does A-level PE involve?

There are three specific components which vary slightly between awarding bodies. Two components of the qualification will be theory based subjects covering topics such as anatomy and physiology, biomechanics, sport psychology, sport sociology and the history of sport. The third component is the practical element based on their personal performance in one activity. This practical component makes up 20% of their grade.

If a student wanted to study for a sports science degree after doing A-levels, which A-levels would complement PE best?

From my experience we had students who chose human biology, psychology and something like mathematics that appeals to universities. Mathematics works well with sports science because of the research element whereby students have to be familiar with mathematics and statistics during the process of research.

If you wanted to be a PE teacher is it preferable to do a four-year PE teaching degree or a three-year sport science degree followed by a one-year postgraduate certificate in education (PGCE)?

Either of these routes is appropriate because in both routes you get training in education – either over a four-year period or condensed into one year. A sports science related degree works well for PE teaching, but you still need to be able to teach a second subject which a PE degree will prepare you for. If you do a PE degree you will have done significant amounts of teaching practice so will have more experience of actually teaching students while sports science graduates will have more in-depth knowledge of scientific concepts they studied on their degrees.

The sports science route is maybe better for students who have not fully decided whether to pursue a career in education and want to keep their options open.

A student interested in teaching needs to decide which age group they want to teach because that will impact on the route, they take in their degree study. A student who wants to teach at primary school level needs to do a degree in education for early years, a secondary school teacher needs to do a PE teaching degree and a student who wants to teach at a Further Education college needs to have a PE degree or a sports science degree and a PGCE which they can often do during their first year of teaching. To teach at university level it is increasingly necessary to have a master's degree and even a PhD as well as your bachelor's degree.

What is the value of a national diploma that specialises in one subject over A-levels that cover a broader range of subjects?

The benefit of A-levels is the breadth or broader study base. You may have three or four subjects to focus on at A-level, so you are not committing to one subject at a relatively young age. A student could start studying a sports science degree and then realise it is not what they want to do. If you have studied a range of A-levels then you have options of subjects that you could study and make a transition to different degree courses relatively smoothly. But if everything is sport focused then any transition would be more difficult. If a student is convinced that sport is the route they want to take, then they should take it, but if they want to keep their options open they should study a range of subjects. At age 16 when a student has finished a range of GCSEs it is a big decision to make, although now they can study a BTEC alongside A-levels.

The counter argument is that the structure of the current BTEC qualifications allow breadth of study with units in anatomy and physiology, psychology and even some business units that could allow entry onto different types of qualification.

It may look like you are committing totally but it may not be the case completely. A-levels students are advised to study A-levels in coherent groups, so you get students taking science A-levels (biology, physics, chemistry), social sciences (psychology and sociology) or humanities (English, French and Spanish). So specialisation is happening at A-level as well. Some students do study a mix of A-levels but not often.

What skills do students learn during A-level study in comparison to BTEC study?

A-level students learn skills such as note taking, essay writing, summarising notes from classes, developing arguments and learning and applying knowledge. BTECs tend to develop independent learning and research skills but only in a good learning environment. If you have a situation where a teacher delivers both A-levels and BTECs you will get the best of both worlds. A-levels are now developed so students get experience of group work and researching topics, but it will never be to the same extent as BTECs because they don't have the time to do it. In A-levels there is so much content to get through that it is a case of reading, learning and then being tested over and over again so time is limited. A-level students are traditionally good at writing essays although this is changing a bit and BTEC students are traditionally good at writing reports and doing presentations.

Finally, I asked David Pears, Senior Lecturer at the University of Bedfordshire, for his view as an admissions tutor on what type of students universities prefer to make offers to.

Do you prefer to make offers to students who have studied A-levels or BTECs?

As an institution we don't have a preference as we look purely at UCAS points. Having taught both types of course I can see that the different students bring different types of things to their studies. BTEC students tend to be more independent in their study. A-level students are more precise and are better at exams because they have had more experience of them. A-level students are taught that to gain marks in exams they have to make sure they provide content that hits the demands of the question and the command verb. So their technique is usually better, and they can work with more precision. What is important is what students do when they get to university and how they engage with lecturers to work with them and become better learners. We want students to get things right first time so we put in opportunities for formative assessment, so they can get some feedback on their work before fully submitting their work. BTECs have put exams in their programmes and this will change and improve things when they get to degree level study.

Other options to access sports careers

For students who do not intend to go to university and don't feel that they are suited to studying A-levels or Level 3 BTEC courses there are additional options to prepare themselves for the workplace.

Technical levels

Technical level qualifications are vocational qualifications that are specifically designed to prepare students for the workplace. They are designed as an alternative to A-levels and are aimed at students aged 16-18. They are available at Levels 2 and 3 and there is a range of subjects to choose from. Cambridge Technicals in Sport and Physical Recreation have been endorsed by the Chartered Institute for the Management of Sport and Physical Recreation (CIMSPA) and Sports Coach UK. They offer Certificates, Diplomas and Extended Diplomas in Sport and Physical Activity which at Level 3 attract UCAS tariff points and can provide entry qualifications for University.

Cambridge Technicals at Level 2 can be studied in a range of vocational areas, such as:

> Assistant Activity Leader
> Assistant Sports Coach
> Assistant Fitness Instructor

The Level 3 Technicals build on the Level 2 awards and include:

> Sports Coaching
> Personal Training
> Recreational Assistant

Technical level qualifications are usually run in Further Education colleges but are also available in some schools.

Just be aware that Technical Level qualifications are different from Tech Awards which are taught in schools for students aged 14-16 and T-levels which are being introduced from September 2020. T-levels will be presented as being equivalent to three A-levels and will involve periods of work placement as well as academic study. T-levels are being planned for sport related subjects.

Apprenticeships

Apprenticeships are where you combine a real, paid job with time allocated for study. An apprentice will work with experienced staff to gain job-specific skills but spend the equivalent of one day a week studying, usually at a local college. Apprentices are expected to spend 30 hours a week working and studying.

Apprenticeships are available in occupations such as sports activity leader, sports coach and personal trainer but they are quite rare, and they may involve significant amounts of travel. Higher level and degree apprenticeships are rarer still, although over time these might start to appear.

Apprenticeships are particularly attractive because you can be paid to work, gain experience and study all at once. There is information on apprenticeship at the government website (GOV.UK) and it is worth looking there to see if there any local apprenticeships available.

National Governing Body of Sports Awards/Short courses

Another route of finding work is to become qualified as a coach in certain sports and then start offering your coaching services to sports centres and schools. There are some excellent companies, such as Premier Sports, who offer after school sports activities and holiday sports camps. They need qualified coaches to run these activities. If you choose this route it is good to have coaching awards in a range of sports so that you are adaptable.

The National Pool Lifeguard Qualification (NPLQ) is a good qualification to have as then you can work as a lifeguard at a leisure or sports centre. It is also good to have the First Aid at Work qualification as often employers will look for this as well as the NPLQ award.

Short courses in fitness instruction and personal training are also good routes into the fitness industry. There are several companies, such as Premier Training and YMCAfit, who offer courses to get you the relevant qualifications. These courses take between two and six weeks and are organised flexibly so you can study full time or part time at weekends. These courses can also be studied with a significant distance learning component. It is often possible to get help with the funding of these courses because they can be expensive.

Before you decide to take this route it would be beneficial to read the earlier section in this chapter. There we discuss the pros and cons of short courses against completing longer degrees or diploma types of study to become a sports coach or personal trainer.

Conclusion

Hopefully you now have some of the information you need to help you make informed choices about your education and your future. I have often heard students say that they don't have time to research all their options or go to open days because they are studying hard and they can worry about that later. To me this is a mindset that is setting yourself up for future problems, such as finding yourself at a university or even in a career that you don't like or doesn't suit you and your personality. As the adage goes – fail to prepare and you prepare to fail!

Making choices can be scary and while I say you need to consider everything before making decisions you also have to realise that wherever you go you will probably have a great time as you will be studying something you love with people who have the same or similar interests to you. People usually study sport because it is something that they are passionate about rather than as a passing interest or something they thought they might like.

Additional resources

Unifrog

https://www.unifrog.org/

Government apprenticeship website

https://www.gov.uk/topic/further-education-skills/apprenticeships

BTEC National qualifications

https://qualifications.pearson.com/en/qualifications/btec-nationals.html

Cambridge Technical Awards

https://www.ocr.org.uk/qualifications/cambridge-technicals/sport-and-physical-activity-2016-suite/

Chapter 2 - Case studies of people working in sport

Introduction

In this chapter you will find 20 interviews of people who are working in sports science and sport related roles. The sports industry is hugely diverse and according to Chartered Institute for the Management of Sport and Physical Recreation (CIMSPA) there are five sectors of work:

- Performance sport and administration
- Exercise and fitness
- Physical activity
- Leisure operations
- Community sport

Within each sector there are multiple occupations and representing each occupation is too large an undertaking for this book. Each of these sectors **is** represented in the interviews I have conducted but I have used different criteria to break them down. When students graduate from sports science degrees they will roughly choose one of four routes.

1. They will work in an area of sports science directly related to their degree with athletes in a sport. This would include occupations such as exercise physiologist, sports coach and strength and conditioning coach.
2. They will work in a sport-related occupation where they are able to use skills and knowledge gained from their degree to a greater or lesser extent. This would include occupations such as teaching or selling sports equipment. This group often have to learn additional skills to carry out their role effectively.
3. They will work in a role entirely unrelated to sport but where they use skills rather than knowledge that they have gained from their degree. Figures vary but around 30% of graduates will work outside of sport after their degree (BASES, 2010).
4. They will remain in education and study for a master's degree or PhD. They may choose to remain in education through a research role.

I have represented the first two groups and looked at careers working in sports science and sport in a broader perspective. Initially, you will find seven interviews of people who are working directly in sports science occupations working with performance athletes. Then you will find interviews from people involved in teaching and coaching before looking at people working in roles as personal trainers and massage therapists. The last five interviews represent people who work in roles related to sport to express the scope and variety of the sports industry. I wanted to show that careers in sport are not limited and that your interest in sport may take you to areas of work that you may not have previously considered.

You may notice that not all these sports related roles are accessed as a result of studying a sports science degree and that some need a specialist degree or a higher qualification. For example, physiotherapy is a popular choice of undergraduate study but to become a physiotherapist you must study physiotherapy as a sports science degree will not give the graduate specific knowledge or the professional skills needed to be a physiotherapist. Likewise, to work as a sports journalist you will need to take a specialised path of study post-degree to gain the skills needed to work in this field. It is important to understand this, so you don't embark on the wrong course of study.

Each interview follows a similar structure with each person being asked about their working role, what it entails, their education and qualifications, their previous experience, what personal skills they need in their role, what advice they would have for students who want to work in these roles and what they like and dislike about their jobs. However, while each interview follows a similar format, there are variations as the interviewees tend to focus on certain areas of their career, or specific to their role and these have been explored in more depth. The aim was to find out as much as possible about each role and get a flavour of what it is like to work in that role.

Some of these working roles will be more interesting to you than others so don't feel you have to read every word of each one and you can select the ones that interest you the most. The interviewees and their working roles are as follows:

1. Emma Gardner – Performance Nutritionist
2. Sarah Murray – Sport and Exercise Psychologist
3. Chris Barry – Sports Analyst
4. Emma Ross – Exercise Physiologist
5. Luke Gupta – Exercise Physiologist and Researcher
6. Will Abbott – Strength and Conditioning Coach
7. Laura Heathcote – Physiotherapist
8. Charlotte Haffenden-Gale – Lecturer in Higher Education
9. Adam Folwell – PE Teacher
10. Richard Horner – F.A. Coach
11. Anthony Limbrick – Football Manager/Head Coach
12. Matt Kleinman – Football Agent
13. Richard Marfell – Personal Trainer/Wellness Coach
14. Ronique Redelinghuys – Personal Trainer/Sports Massage Therapist
15. Lisa Kelly – Sports Massage Therapist
16. Alistair Bruce-Ball – Sports Broadcaster (BBC Radio 5 Live)

17. Adam Leitch – Sports Journalist
18. Vicki Galvin – Sport and Physical Activity Manager
19. Nik Elphick – Sports Equipment Sales
20. Grace Kelly – Outdoor Pursuits Instructor

Interview 1
Emma Gardner

Performance Nutritionist

Name

Emma Gardner

Job title

Performance Nutritionist at the English Institute of Sport (EIS).

Qualifications

BSc (Hons) Sport and Exercise Science, Birmingham University

MSc Sport and Exercise Science (Psychology pathway), Manchester Metropolitan University

MSc Sports Nutrition, London Metropolitan University

IOC Diploma in Sports Nutrition

Introduction

Emma is lead performance nutritionist at the English Institute of Sport based at Bisham Abbey. She works with the GB women's hockey team who won the gold medal at the 2016 Olympic Games in Rio de Janeiro. She also works with the England Cricket team who won the Men's World Cup in 2019. She has previously worked with other teams including Northampton Saints Rugby Union club.

What does a performance nutritionist do?

Put simply a nutritionist advises athletes on what they should be eating, how much and how often. However, to do this they need to understand the energy demands of a sport and the effect that a sport has on the structures of the body. There is also the biochemical balance of each individual's body and their eating preferences to consider.

Roughly speaking an athlete will eat or drink around 2000 times a year and each time the biochemical balance of the body will be affected positively or negatively. The aim of the performance nutritionist is to increase the number of nutritional moments which have a positive effect and reduce the number that have a negative effect. If an athlete is influencing their biochemistry positively these moments build up and will enhance their performance, reduce their risk of injury and promote their wellness. Performance Nutritionists will design strategies that promote the best adaptations to training and contribute to performance enhancement.

However, every athlete is different in terms of the demands they place on their body during training and competition. They will have their own food preferences and habits as to when they like to eat. The performance nutritionist needs to assess these demands and build a nutritional strategy that considers all these variables. Added to that is the issue of the availability of food when travelling abroad and adapting diet to the availability of food.

Tell me about your education?

At school I did A-levels in sports studies, psychology, biology and art. I applied for a degree in Sport and Exercise Science at Birmingham University and they wanted three science A-levels. They were happy to accept sports studies and psychology as sciences, in addition to the biology and I got the grades I needed.

The good thing for me about the degree at Birmingham was that you started studying broadly by covering nutrition, psychology, biomechanics and physiology and then in your second and third years you could opt for a choice of modules. After completing my degree, I applied to do a PhD in Neuropsychology and would have had a very different career if I'd gone down that route. But at that point I wasn't too sure what I wanted to specialise in, so I decided to do a Sport and Exercise Science Master's degree at Manchester Metropolitan University and specialised in sport psychology. The course included a foundation branch in physiology which included nutrition, so I studied that as well. After my master's degree, I got a job as a sport scientist working for Lucozade Sport and because of my previous studies I specialised in the nutrition route.

Then I joined the English Institute of Sport (EIS) and studied for the IOC Diploma in Sports Nutrition. This took me two years and I was able to convert it into a master's degree at London Metropolitan University. There is a cluster of five or six universities who will accept the IOC diploma and allow you to convert it into a master's degree. London Metropolitan allowed me to study at a distance which was lucky as I was working full time. I had an induction, was assigned a tutor and completed my dissertation without having to attend any research methods lectures. I already had credits in research methods from my previous master's and they developed a pathway for me to submit my dissertation and get a second master's degree.

What are the entry requirements for the IOC diploma in sports nutrition?

You need a degree in sports science or a related discipline, such as food nutrition or dietetics, or anything along those lines. It is an online two-year distance learning course run by lecturers in sports nutrition.

What are your daily duties and responsibilities?

Our job at the EIS is to ensure athletes are fit for purpose. That sounds very broad but as a performance nutritionist we must ensure that athletes are optimally educated and have strategies in place to enable them to train and compete at the highest level. My day to day responsibilities are to look after the athletes' nutritional needs but my job varies for professional and Olympic sports people as they operate in very different environments. For example, I will see Olympic sports people for one-to-one work, or I will see them if they are injured or have performance issues. I may do some broad education sessions for entire groups and work to prepare them for competition.

Olympic sport performers, such as the hockey players, will have two to four competitions a year and an Olympics every four years. However, in professional sport, the athletes are performing every week, so my job becomes about their day to day recovery and ensuring they have appropriate fuelling strategies. But there are other aspects of our role with regard to managing athletes' supplementation protocols, nutritional strategies for athletes competing overseas as well as working in a team of multidisciplinary practitioners. When working with teams and individuals we use a collaborative approach to plan training and prepare for competition. I will work closely with the physiologists, strength and conditioning coaches, psychologists and doctors to ensure a joined-up approach to the preparation of athletes to ensure we provide them the best support we can.

What did you do before working for EIS?

After my master's degree I was still unsure what I wanted to do as despite having specialised in psychology I was still interested in physiology. So I started to look for sport science jobs by typing 'sport science jobs' into search engines. This brought up a whole range of options which included jobs on the BASES website and sports development officers working for county councils. Then I saw a job as a sports scientist working for Lucozade Sport. This job involved supporting teams and individuals who used and promoted Lucozade products, such as professional teams or sports centres that had a Lucozade sport vending machine or sports stores that stocked Lucozade products. My job was to develop product knowledge and explain why people would need an electrolyte drink and when they would use it. There were other aspects to the role, such as educating people about urine analysis, sweat patches and using speed gates for fitness testing. For example, we would do some fitness testing and then link the test results back to nutrition and describe its impact on performance.

My week was very varied, for example, one day I could be educating 50 salespeople who were going to a gym chain to sell products and explain the science behind each product. The next day I could be going to an evening at a running club to explain why they need a carbohydrate gel and then I would go running with them. I did the job for three years and during that time I got some insights into professional sports, such as boxing, and I started providing one-to-one advice to individual athletes. I had a big moment when I realised that working one-to-one and providing individualised advice was what I actually enjoyed doing and as a result decided that working in the applied side of nutrition was what I wanted to do.

I had heard about the English Institute of Sport (EIS) and was aware they employed many different types of practitioners. I had already met a member of the EIS nutrition team, and he had told me about paid internships that the EIS offered. I applied for a 12-month paid internship at Bisham Abbey to learn about working in elite sport. I was fortunate to get a position just before the 2012 Olympics.

Are internships common in elite sport?

At EIS we have four or five nutritionists who started working with us through internships, including the current head of the performance nutrition team. Internships are common within the EIS but the attraction for me was that it was paid. Many internships in elite sport are unpaid and this can be difficult when you are also working and trying to cope financially. Recently we have started working with universities to move towards student placements which are part of their formal education, rather than offering internships. Students study for their master's degree whilst also working for us, some universities offer this s part of a placement module. We also have several PhD students who are funded jointly by the EIS and their universities as they are conducting research to answer specific performance questions for us. They have a dual role as while they are working to complete their doctorate they are placed with us for one or two days a week to work with athletes in a specific sport. For example, we had one student who was working with the triathlon squad and researching the role of calcium intake on the prevalence of stress fractures. This enabled her to do a PhD in applied sport and also work during her studies.

What advice would you have for students who want a similar career to yours?

The biggest thing for me was that I wanted to do something as a career that I enjoyed. I always remember what a lecturer said to me when I was studying for my first master's degree. I was feeling a bit lost as I didn't know what I wanted to do. He said, 'my advice is pick something you enjoy doing because you are going to spend a long time working'. He also said, 'if thinking about work on Monday ever stops you doing something on Sunday then you know you are in the wrong job'. With these things in mind, I said I know I enjoy sport and working with people and the glimpses I've had of working with athletes are the parts I've really enjoyed. My advice would be to pick a subject that you have a genuine interest in because then you will be committed to it. I know I am fortunate because 99% of my work doesn't feel like work as it is enjoyable and fun. Every day is different for me as my job is so varied. If you want a 9-5 job that is repetitive and predictable then working in elite sport is probably not for you.

My other advice is to have a mentor as this is critical to your personal development. I have always had mentors, although not always one directly linked to nutrition. I had a brilliant mentor who was my manager at Lucozade Sport and after I left we stayed in touch. He was very much someone I could go to and ask for advice and bounce ideas off. He was someone outside my work setting and not invested in what I was doing day to day. That was very important.

Lastly, it may be clichéd but try and get as much experience as you can. We get hundreds of applicants who want to do this job and ultimately, we need to find ways to differentiate between them. So, when you do your application make sure you pay attention to detail and take your time over your CV to really think about how what you have done applies to what this job is asking you to do. Try and get opportunities to work with athletes as there are thousands of sports science graduates and you need to stand out. People who have experience of working with athletes and have developed their soft skills, such as communication and listening, have an advantage because they have an awareness of what this environment is like and its demands.

What soft skills do you need in your role?

Communication and being able to manipulate your style to communicate with different practitioners and athletes is massively important. I work with 33 female hockey players who are all very different, they come from different backgrounds, have different reasons why they are hockey players and different drivers as to why they do this for a living. Some of them love to talk about nutrition, others who think it has no relation to them in any shape or form to their hockey performance. Your big challenge is to apply the amazing knowledge you have gained from your studies to their specific requirements but if you can't put it into meaningful terms for an athlete it has no value. You have to find ways to communicate with athletes and build rapport with them to get them to change their nutritional behaviour.

Sometimes I alter my approach by not even talking about nutrition for the first 20 minutes of a consultation and I'll try and make them feel comfortable by talking about things that are going on in their life. There are other athletes who want to talk about the findings of specific research papers and how they can be applied. It's about reading different situations and you need to have self-awareness and emotional intelligence to do this. These can be developed over time by working in different environments and with different people. Building relationships and communicating well are hugely important to my role. Being able to read situations is important when you working as part of a large team of practitioners and you need to think broadly about how your discipline impacts on the other disciplines.

You've got the additional issue as a nutritionist of setting an example as well. This must be difficult at times?

It can be and it is funny as strength and conditioning coaches say you wouldn't want a personal trainer that doesn't train themselves and it's similar with nutrition. As much as we aren't the athlete I will always try and set an example for the athletes by looking after myself and my nutrition. Fortunately, I eat well and enjoy training. But yes, the eyes are always on you.

You also mentioned motivation and you have an understanding of psychology.

I have found that there is a huge overlap between nutrition and psychology. Eating well and appropriately for performance can often involve athletes undergoing behaviour change which is a psychological issue. So I need to develop strategies to support the athlete's change in behaviour. It is also important to understand motivation and I'll often ask people I work with is 'why do you do this, what drives you to be an athlete?' For some people, they say 'I want to be the best that I can be' but other people say, 'I need to make a living, I need to pay the bills', or, 'I just fell into it as I happen to be talented at it'. Once you understand an athlete's motivation and what drives them it helps shape how you encourage them to change behaviour. I work in team sports and one week I worked with 125 athletes across five days. I try to make the effort to get to know each individual and make the effort to understand every one. If you get to know athletes on a personal level and you understand someone well you can work better with them. Having the skills to get to know someone makes your life easier as a practitioner.

I've always said that it is important for a student to know what they want to study but for your job you need to have a broad knowledge.

That's right, I need to understand physiology, psychology, biomechanics and the demands of sport so it is important to have a broad base of knowledge before narrowing your field down. One of the first questions we ask in an interview is 'tell me about the needs analysis of this sport and its physiological requirements?' This is to see if the person has done their homework but also to see if they understand what aspects they are trying to impact on. Nutritional needs differ depending on the sport you are working in and while you don't need to be a specialist in that sport you do need to understand its physical demands.

Are there any parts of your job that you don't enjoy or like less?

Yes! There are aspects I don't like. For example, if the food on offer somewhere isn't good I get the blame. Athletes get confused and think you are also the chef so if there are any problems related to food athletes will complain to you; especially when they are travelling.

Often athletes are trying to lower their skinfold scores (measurement of body fat) and if they don't then as the nutritionist you are the person who the blame falls on. Our job is to give advice and support athletes as they make changes, but they are the ones that have to do it. I don't enjoy when the finger is pointed in my direction because something has not changed, or an athlete has become frustrated because you have given them advice that's not working. That is when our job becomes challenging because you've got to find other strategies to get the end result. I love 99% of the job but like any job there are bits you don't enjoy, such as dealing with the numerous emails. When you are working with 120 athletes you need to find a lot of time for admin work.

In terms of the future how do you see your career development?

It is important to always develop and always be pushed. Every year we review our work and set objectives to improve and we are given a certain amount of continuous professional development (CPD) time to pursue our development objectives. For me personally, I want to get into management and leadership and explore the psychology aspects of nutrition further. Even though I am now a nutritionist I like learning about the other aspects of practice that impact on the advice we deliver. For example, this year I have highlighted that I want to go on a communication and leadership course to learn how to lead and manage groups. Behaviour change is also an area that I am looking to learn more about. No matter what level a person is working at it is critical to develop yourself and review back by reflecting on performance. At the EIS, it is mandatory to review performance and every year every single member of the institute will have an appraisal. We use 360-degree feedback where we ask our colleagues to appraise us, which is really good and allows you to take time to reflect on how you are doing in your job and what you could do better.

Additional resources

IOC Diploma in nutrition

http://www.sportsoracle.com/Nutrition/About+the+Program/

English Institute of Sport

http://www.eis2win.co.uk/

Open University free course in Nutrition

https://www.open.edu/openlearn/health-sports-psychology/health/the-science-nutrition-and-healthy-eating/content-section-overview?active-tab=content-tab

Interview 2

Sarah Murray

Sport and Exercise Psychologist

Name

Sarah Murray

Job title

Lead Sport and Exercise Psychologist for Brighton and Hove Albion Football Club Academy

Senior Lecturer in Sport Psychology at the University of Chichester

Qualifications

BSc (Hons) Sport and Exercise Science, University of Brighton

PGCE (Secondary Education), University of Brighton

MSc Sport Psychology, Brunel University

BASES accredited Sport and Exercise Scientist (Psychology)

Introduction

Sarah is the sport psychologist at Brighton and Hove Albion Football Club where she has responsibility for the Academy players. The Academy consists of age group players from Under-9s up to Under-23s. She is also a senior lecturer at the University of Chichester where she lectures part time in Applied Sport Psychology.

What does a sport psychologist do?

A sport psychologist will work with individuals and teams to help them prepare psychology for the demands of competition and training. Sport psychologists have many different roles and they work to develop a positive mind set and mental toughness in athletes. They will also teach athletes skills that they can use to overcome stress and anxiety and develop self-confidence and motivation. Sport psychologists are involved in ensuring athlete welfare, or wellness, as well as preparing them for performance. This is because athletes who operate in high performance environments can experience issues related to stress and pressure.

While a lot of sport psychology is proactive, or about preparation, sport psychologists also have to be reactive and may have to help athletes deal with difficult situations, such as injury, overcoming disappointments or accepting criticism.

Sports psychologists also work with teams where they can work on team development, team dynamics and developing team goals. They will spend a lot of time with the team and become immersed in the team environment and be able to react when things don't work out as planned.

Did you know what you wanted to do when you studied for your degree?

I always knew what I was going to do with my degree once I had graduated but that is quite rare. I am also one of the few sports students who stayed to work in sport after graduating. Most people that I know with a sports science degree do nothing with it related to sport or science. A degree shows that you can study to a certain level and we are in a world where we are not so prescriptive about having to do certain degrees for certain jobs. People seem to have more than one career in their lifetime, particularly the millennials will have more than one career. It used to be that a career was for life and now it's barely for Christmas.

Tell me about your education.

I did nine GCSEs, including physical education and then A-levels in physical education (P.E.), English literature and sociology. I didn't do science type subjects at A-Level as I was good with language and words. They may not have been particularly scientific, but they link massively to the work I do now as a sport psychologist. A-levels show you can study to a certain level and I had to work really hard to get grade Bs and Cs. In fact, I didn't get the grades I needed for university, so had to take a gap year to retake one exam and do some travelling.

I knew I wanted to teach P.E. but I also knew I didn't want to do a teaching degree. I wanted to do a sports science degree followed by a PGCE (Post Graduate Certificate in Education). I knew that doing a sport science degree would give me more life options while doing a standard teaching degree might limit my future career options.

I did a sports science degree at the University of Brighton and I loved it. The most interesting part for me was always the sport psychology. I then did a PGCE in secondary education at Brighton and was a P.E. teacher for eight years. I always knew that I didn't want to teach for the rest of my life, or be a head teacher, and I didn't have any aspirations beyond head of department. I'd always thought I'd like to go down the sport psychology route at some point but thought that would be in my late 30s rather than late 20s. So, I took a year out to teach part-time while I did a Master's degree in Sport Psychology at Brunel University.

After that the plan was to carry on with my teaching career and have this extra qualification, but I loved my master's so much that I wanted to move into the world of sport psychology and work as an applied sport psychologist. I picked up a four day a week job as a P.E. teacher and that gave me time to develop my BASES (British Association of Sport and Exercise Sciences) accreditation. I did a three-year BASES supervision to become a qualified sport and exercise scientist (psychology). It was a bit like doing a PGCE for three years in a row, producing evidence and building a client base. By the third year I had given up teaching altogether as I had set up my own business as a freelance sport psychologist. I was working with athletes from grass roots level to elite level and coaches across any number of different sports. In 2013 I got a full-time job with Brighton and Hove Albion. After four years there it became apparent that there was far too much work for just one person, so I asked if I could go part-time and employ another sport psychologist. At this point I was also offered a senior lecturer's role in sport psychology at the University of Chichester for one day a week.

I am now head of department at Brighton and Hove Albion in sport psychology and I lecture one day a week in Applied Sport Psychology at University of Chichester. I worked for four years as they only sport psychologist at Brighton and for a while was one of the only full-time sport psychologists working in academy football. Football was late in adopting sport psychologists but has caught up since. To get someone else into the department I cut back my hours and this has created a much better working environment. There are now two of us with the academy and a third sport psychologist working with the women's team.

What does your sport psychology work typically involve?

The average working week is six to seven days and two or three of those days can be working both day and evening, either 8 am to 8 pm or 9 am to 9 pm. I get 20 day's leave a year but can only take those in the off season.

A typical day would involve working predominantly with coaches and supporting them. If there is only one sport psychologist and a lot of athletes, the best way to filter information to athletes is through the coaches. I also do one-to-one sessions with players from the under 9s to U23s and I do squad sessions with players, usually educating them on sport psychology topics. I also run a performance parenting programme working with the parents of elite athletes which is very important. I will be involved in all decisions about the retain and release of players as part of the multidisciplinary team we have, along with the physiotherapists and sports scientists we have here. I am involved in writing reports on players, screening them and testing them two to three times a season. I go on pre-season tours with the squads as part of the team and work with other members of the multidisciplinary team, particularly with the physiotherapists regarding the psychology of sports injury.

Do you use observation a lot during your work?

I do observe a lot during training and matches and it may be player focused or coach focused. For example, I may watch the coach's body language or how they are communicating. I may watch a player for something specific and then write up reports. I am always at training and games and I'm involved in everything.

What other sport scientist roles are there at Brighton and Hove Albion?

In the academy (U9s to U23s) we have four full-time strength and conditioning coaches and four physiotherapists. In the first team they will also have full-time sports massage therapists and a team doctor. We also have three sports analysts that I work closely with and a couple of interns. There are similar numbers of these roles for the first team.

You also work at the University of Chichester. Is it typical for sport psychologists to also work in academia?

Whilst the dream of a sport psychologist may be to combine applied work and high-level academia there are only a handful who can do this type of job and lecture as well. It is more common that a sport psychologist will work in research and not do applied work, or they will be fully immersed in the applied world and have nothing to do with research or teaching. Due to my teaching background I quite fancied doing some lecturing because I love to teach. I teach one day a week but see my world as being the applied world. My role at Chichester is to lecture on the applied modules and bring the real world of sport psychology to the students because I am in it while the other lecturers aren't.

That is a useful differentiation and shows the diversity of working in sport psychology.

Yes, the skill sets are different as you may have a person who has researched and written a lot of academic papers, but they just don't have the skills needed for applied consultancy and work one-to-one with athlete experiencing a specific issue. It's just a different skill set.

What skills do you think you need to be an applied sport psychologist?

You need very high levels of self-awareness about why you are doing the job. You have to ask yourself, 'what is your why?' or 'why am I doing this?'. You must have this sense of purpose and a focus on the love of the job. It may sound cheesy but if you are doing this work for money it probably won't work out as you won't make any more than you need to get a mortgage and run a car. The income is very average, so you have to have a real focus on supporting athletes and the rewards that this. You have to be able to deal with multiple types of people and connect with people from different age groups, sporting backgrounds, academic backgrounds. Some people you work with may have doctorates (PhDs) and high academic knowledge, but most will have great sporting knowledge, but less scientific knowledge and you need to be able to communicate with them on their level. Communication skills are key because you have to be able to communicate what you are doing to other people. Also, you need to have high levels of personal organisation because you are often juggling the demands of lots of clients. You may also be working with athletes in a number of different sports as it's rare just to be working in the one. You also need adaptability.

Why is adaptability so important?

All situations are different and often you don't know what situation you are walking into. You have to adapt your behaviour to the situation and the needs of those around you. Those people who have asked you to be there may not necessarily know why they want you there, as while most coaches value you as a sport psychologist they don't always know what exactly you are going to do. You need to be able to assess a situation and build good relationships very quickly.

Building relationships seems key to your role – how do you go about developing relationships?

I listen to people and give them my time. I take on board exactly what they want from me. As sport scientists we like to blind people with science. This is okay if we've already got a relationship with them but as a starting point we need to recognise that all relationships are human to human. If you can get the relationship right, then afterwards you can do all the blinding them with science you like as then they'll take it on board.

It took me about five years at Brighton before the coaches and everyone else really knew what it was that I did, and they now come to me rather than me having to go to them. They come and ask me, 'what do you think about this?', 'how do you think this could work?' But it has taken five years to build up the relationships to this point. It doesn't matter if you are a sport psychologist, sport scientist or a business manager, working with other people is about developing relationships. That is something that you don't learn at university. Generally speaking at university you don't learn about how to do the job. For example, when I finished my master's I remember thinking 'wow, that was so inspirational, I loved studying for it but what hell does a sport psychologist do – I've absolutely no idea!'

Did you have to find your own way?

I found my own style of working through my BASES supervision but without that I wouldn't have. Luckily you can't call yourself a sport psychologist unless you have been through a supervision programme.

Most people don't know what you need to do to call yourself a sport psychologist. You cannot do a master's in sport psychology and call yourself a sport psychologist. Just as you can't do a master's in English Literature and then call yourself an English teacher because you are not. The term 'sport psychologist' is protected and you can only call yourself a sport psychologist is you have gained British Psychological Society (BPS) chartership or are registered with the Health and Care Professions Council (HCPC).

Do you think there has been a move from trainee sport psychologists doing a sport science degree towards doing a psychology degree?

I think there was but in 2008 the traditional training route for sport psychology in this country changed. Historically, sport psychologists were always produced through BASES making it very sports based with people with strong sporting backgrounds and sport science degrees. In 2008 the British Psychological Society (BPS) took the title 'sport psychologist' and became the main training provider. The problem was that more and more people with psychology backgrounds were becoming interested in sport psychology and those with sport science backgrounds were thinking 'what's the point as I can't do my BPS training because I haven't got a pure psychology background.' Now some time in 2019 BASES are going to apply to Health Care Professions Council (HCPC) recognition so if you train through BASES or BPS you may be able to call yourself a sport psychologist. So, it is encouraging both routes. That is important because a person with a sport or sport science background can bring a lot to the applied world. This is because you have to talk the language of the athletes and the coaches and you know what pressure and stress are like and you can only get this from being involved in sport yourself.

It has definitely helped me that I have a strong performance background having played National League hockey. While it doesn't make me a great sport psychologist it does add to what I do as I have always been immersed in the world of sport – it's my comfort zone. For someone who hasn't any experience in elite sport it can be a really tough place to be. Particularly for a female sport psychologist in a predominantly male football club.

What is the importance of the HCPC recognition?

Without the Health Care Professions Council qualification doctors, physiotherapists and general psychologists cannot practice. Currently you can only be HCPC registered if you have done the BPS training route not the BASES route. This will hopefully change in 2019.

What advice would give to someone who was interested in becoming a sport psychologist?

Definitely have a really big goal like working with elite teams or working at Olympic Games as that is great. But never underestimate the power of working with any athlete at any level in terms of how that can develop you as a practitioner. Don't be elitist because all experiences will feed into the becoming the practitioner you will become. A lot of my students only want to work with elite athletes, but if you are going to do that you need experience and that comes from working with a young golfer or at the tennis club down the road. For me it was never about working with elite athletes. It was about doing it for the love of the job which has in turn led me to work with elite athletes. It's now my passion but working with elite athletes was never the be all and end all for me.

Additional resources

Health Care Professions Council (HCPC)

https://www.hcpc-uk.org/registration/

British Psychological Society

https://www.bps.org.uk/

Open University free course in sport psychology

https://www.open.edu/openlearn/health-sports-psychology/exploring-sport-coaching-and-psychology/content-section-overview?active-tab=description-tab

Interview 3

Chris Barry

Performance analyst

Name

Chris Barry

Job title:

Performance Analyst

Qualifications

BSc (Hons) Physiology and Sports Science, Glasgow University

Introduction

Chris Barry is the performance analyst for the English Institute of Sport for five years and works with the British Judo team at the Centre of Excellence in Walsall. He has been involved in Judo as a performer for the last 23 years.

What does a performance analyst do?

A performance analyst will provide relevant key performance information to athletes and coaches during and after performance. Information is provided to improve performance through understanding and improving techniques, movement and tactics within a sport. Athletes and coaches can find it difficult to recall in detail what has happened during competition and a performance analyst will provide objective information through a range of performance data. This is done through a four-stage process called capture-code-analyse-feedback.

A performance analyst will be able to assess the demands of a sport or different positions within a team sport and model what is needed to be successful in that sport. They can measure the techniques and tactics of the best performers and then compare them against the athletes they are working with and provide guidance on how athletes can improve and develop.

Performance analysts will also provide information, referred to as pre-competition intelligence, that helps athletes prepare for opponents by analysing their strengths and weaknesses. They will use software, such as Dartfish Video Analysis, to capture athletes' performances and analyse them. Performance analysts will be part of a performance team that supports coaches and athletes during training.

Tell me about your education

Being educated in Scotland I did Highers and Advanced Highers. For my Highers I did maths, English, physics, chemistry and biology and an Advanced Higher in chemistry. I then did a BSc (Hons) Physiology and Sports Science at Glasgow University which was a four-year degree as all degrees are in Scotland.

At the end of the second year I applied for an internship to work as a performance analyst at Glasgow Warriors. I did this alongside my degree for the last two years and another two years after I had finished studying. I worked with the Scottish National Rugby team as well providing sport science support, including GPS monitoring and wellness monitoring. I got great experience during my degree and the degree itself also gave me a really good understanding of all the other support disciplines.

Tell me about your current role and what your job entails?

I am heavily involved in analysing data from competitions and normally there will have been a competition at the weekend and there will be data to be analysed. That will occupy the beginning of my week as well as adding the videos from the weekend's competition to the database of performances. Usually I'll have quite a few projects running on individual athletes and because there are different fighting styles, weight categories and differences in genders there is no set template used to analyse a judo player. These projects are based on what individual athletes are trying to develop. I also analyse the upcoming opposition and update our database to ensure we are ready for the next fights. I give in-training support to coaches who may be working with an athlete to develop something technical.

There is a camera in the dojo where we train that allows us to show replays. An athlete can perform their moves, have a look at themselves and then adjust if necessary and do it again. I might be asked to find and show examples of world class athletes performing the same move.

Also I am involved in multidisciplinary teamwork, as we have support staff meetings periodically to check and regulate the work we do with each athlete to make sure it is aligned to the athlete's individual programmes and their plan. An athlete's plan for what they are developing, and their goals is for the whole year. We identify any barriers to their progress and identify potential solutions. I spend a lot of time in my week sitting and talking to coaches, as I see that as a hugely important part of my role to build the relationship and discuss their work. It might not be about judo but about them and what they are doing as building relationships is one of the most important things you do as support staff. As a performance analyst you have to be trusted by coaches and be relied upon to produce material that is relevant to their athletes.

We have some multidisciplinary projects, for example, at the moment we have a project looking at the injury risks for individual athletes. There are some athletes whose style of judo is less conventional and riskier than other athletes. We need to understand the risks posed by the positions that these risky athletes put themselves and see if there are technical tweaks we can make, or we've got to figure out how to make them strong within that unusual range of movement. This can involve strength and conditioning coaches, judo coaches, analysts, physiotherapists and the collaboration of the whole of the support staff.

What technology do you use for performance analysis in judo?

We've got two CCTV cameras that we attach on the walls of the dojo to give two different angles. These are connected to a Wi-Fi router, so we can relay video images to a laptop and use Dartfish software to analyse performance. We can get an athlete to perform a technique and then watch it themselves or we can record it and analyse it later on. The other things I use to capture competition tend to be from an internet stream, so I'll use a media box that allows me to screen capture and if I'm in the arena I'm able to capture through the media box directly into my laptop. Dartfish and Microsoft Excel are the tools I use the most.

Do you need to have an in-depth knowledge of the sport you are analysing?

That varies a little bit as some sports, such as timed sports, you may not need to know so well. You have to understand the rules and what it takes to win at the sport, but it depends on the sport whether you need to be an absolute expert in it. Judo is one that is very technical as it is an open skilled, combat sport that is objectively judged and these things require you to know a lot about the sport. However, if you take track cycling, while it may be quite tactical the analysis mostly involves data analysis, such as looking at power and times. It does depend on the sport and it can't do you any harm knowing about the sport. The main thing is to remain as objective as you can and take any bias out of it which can be difficult as it is sometimes difficult to identify your own biases and then let them not affect your judgement.

What skills do you need to work as a performance analyst?

The first and foremost skill is developing relationships between yourself and others because without relationship it is pretty difficult to be impactful when discussing technical skills. There are technical skills that you need to do the job but the glue that binds it together is the personal side.

Communication is one of the biggest skills you need, and it does not involve only how you deliver information but also how you receive it. A coach may want a certain thing analysed but you need to get them to be as explicit as possible with their request. If I try and infer something from what they are saying rather than actually listen to them then I may produce something that they don't want. This can waste my time and theirs, damage that relationship and produce a negative outcome. Receiving information is hugely important and so you need to make sure that coaches are explicit in asking for what they want. There is often a bit of creativity required, like when you are trying to land a message with someone you need to be creative about how you send that message. What works for some will not work with others, so you need to be creative and figure out ways that will resonate with somebody to get your message across.

Being able to read a situation by having social and emotional intelligence to read a room and assess what people are thinking and feeling is so important. Then you can decide whether you want to add anything to the conversation or decide to keep quiet. In the world of sport, people come and go quite quickly so you need to be able to be adaptable to deal with that and work out who the key stakeholders **are**, so you know who to keep satisfied and ensure you still have a job. If you don't satisfy the key stakeholders, they are unlikely to keep you on.

Also, you need to be adaptable to changing situations in the competitive environment. For example, at the Paralympics in 2016 almost every time I set up in the arena someone came over and said, 'you can't be here, you need to move your stuff'. There are ways to deal with this – you can have a plan when you arrive, or you can argue if there is a problem! I tend to argue at first, then try to negotiate or failing that rely on bribery. I managed to bribe a steward to let me stay where I shouldn't have technically been by giving him a GB team pin badge. He was happy with that and let me stay there for the whole tournament. Being able to negotiate with people who aren't that receptive to what you are trying to do is a very important personal skill.

Another important skill is being reflective, so you can look back at something you have done and how you have done it in that situation, assess it and see what you could have done differently and then implement any changes from your reflection later on. It may have been that you had an argument with someone in a meeting, how did you act in that situation and how could I avoid that kind of confrontation in the future. Being able to reflect on situations and learn from them can make you a better practitioner in the long run.

How do other sports scientists feed into your work as a performance analyst?

There is crossover with strength and conditioning, nutrition and psychology. For example, there was a fight in the 2017 World Championships that was a marathon of a fight that went to a golden score. Bear in mind that the normal time for a fight lasts for four minutes and it went on for twice as long as the normal time in addition to the four minutes of the normal time. It was a really heavy load on their bodies and the standard of the contest was through the roof and the demands on their bodies to perform like for that duration of time that was incredible.

We did some analysis on the length of exchanges in that contest from when the referee started it to each time they stopped it and reset them. We looked at the overall duration, how many long exchanges did they have back-to-back and then looked at what happened in those exchanges. We then get an idea about how training can be planned to either meet those demands or exceed them and then you are ready for any situation that may arise. Then we are able to inform strength and conditioning coaches to prepare the athlete for the potential intensity and duration of fights, the physiotherapist can look at strengthening specific joints for an athlete executing moves specific to them. Because I have all the video I can assess it and help physiotherapists with their diagnosis and also the rehabilitation of any injuries. As for the role of the sport psychologist, their plan for the athlete is to have specific interventions for when they are on the mat. I can look out for when they use these interventions and feed back to the sport psychologist on how effective they were.

What advice would you have for a student who wanted to become a performance analyst?

I would suggest going through formal undergraduate education but ensure that any programme you are enrolling on has some form of practical placement on it or actively encourages you find work placement. Theory is only good if it is put into practice. You need to have the experience and have the opportunities to learn about building relationships and find out what it is like working with individuals and within different organisations.

Additional resources

Dartfish analysis package

https://www.dartfish.com/

Sportscode analytics

http://sportscode.com/analytics/

Interview 4

Emma Ross

Exercise Physiologist

Name

Dr. Emma Ross

Job title

Head of Physiology at English Institute of Sport

Qualifications

BSc (Hons) Sport and Exercise Sciences, Exeter University

MSc in Coaching Science, University of Wales Institute Cardiff

PhD in Exercise Neurophysiology, Brunel University

Introduction

Emma leads a team of physiologists at the English Institute of Sport who support some of the best athletes in the world. She has been responsible for leading and managing the physiology team through the most successful Olympic and Paralympic cycle in British Olympic history (2012-2016). She is currently working to deliver the physiology strategy for the Tokyo Olympic Games in 2020.

What does an exercise physiologist do?

Basically a physiologist will assess the physiological demands of a sport and assess what physical characteristics an athlete in that sport requires to be successful when competing at the highest level. For example, what is needed in terms of an athlete's speed, power, endurance, strength and flexibility. Once the physiological demands of a sport have been established then the physiologist will measure how an athlete performs in tests that have been designed to measure these characteristics. Once these assessments have been made then the physiologist can advise the coach and athlete about training and preparation for competition. They may also advise on things like rest, recovery and sleep. A physiologist often works with a sports nutritionist to advise on diet for recovery and a physiotherapist for athletes who are recovering from injury.

Another important role is assessing how the body responds and adapts to exercise in different environments, such as hot and cold environments or altitude. This is vital for preparing athletes for international competition which may be held in environments that are significantly different to the UK's.

A physiologist has to have detailed knowledge of the workings of the human body and the different biological systems – cardiovascular, respiratory, muscular, skeletal and nervous system. Also detailed knowledge of how these respond and adapt to exercise is essential. In addition to this they have to understand a battery of different physiological tests and measurements and be able to analyse and assess the value of these results.

In terms of personal skills, they will need to be able to communicate information to coaches and athletes effectively and efficiently in a language that they can understand. They have to be adaptable and able to solve problems in situations that can be complex.

Physiologists have to be able to translate research findings into actions that will promote the success of athletes. They need to constantly update themselves on recent research findings and assess the implications of research on their practice. Physiologists are often involved in research themselves and contributing to the body of knowledge in the subject and pushing the boundaries.

Why did you choose to work in sport?

Sport has always been a significant part of my life and it has served me really well personally and professionally. I have always been really interested in sports performance and want to know what makes people run faster or what makes one team of hockey players better than another. I don't always know a lot about some of the sports that I work with, but I just have a real interest in humans doing sport. If you want to work in sport it is really important that you love sport and are passionate about it.

Tell me about your education

I did A-levels in geography, English and biology. By doing geography and biology I got a sense of scientific enquiry and English helped me to learn to communicate through writing, whether it was essays, academic papers or presentations.

Then I went on to do a sports science degree at Exeter University. I already loved and played a lot of sport but having done a couple of science A-levels I also began to enjoy the science side. I have noticed that some students who study sports science just like sport and are less interested in the science that comes with it. You won't get through a sports science degree if you just like sport and are not interested in science as well.

I really wanted to go to Exeter University and loved the course there but when I finished, I had no idea what I wanted to do. I had started my sports science degree thinking I might like to be a P.E. teacher and although I hadn't ruled it out, at that point I didn't want to do a PGCE. That as much as anything directed me towards a master's degree and because I could write well, and my written work was good enough, my lecturers recognised that I could go on and do a master's degree.

I ended up going to University of Wales Institute in Cardiff to study for my master's degree. I was playing rugby at the time and they had a really good rugby team, so I went there more for the opportunity to play rugby than for the course. Having completed my master's in coaching science I got a scholarship to do a PhD at Brunel University which was a funded place. That was brilliant because I had the opportunity to teach alongside doing my doctorate and I think teaching is really valuable. When you teach you've got to really know your subject inside out so you can pass the knowledge on other people. At the EIS we find that people who have the best physiology knowledge are people who have spent a couple of years teaching after university as teaching forces you to know your subject in-depth and broadly. I did my doctorate in neuromuscular physiology and exercise and then I did what seems to be a normal thing for a PhD student is to say that now I'm in academia I'll stay here a while as it's fun. I get to keep learning and I really enjoy teaching. I stayed until I got a lecturer post at Brunel teaching exercise physiology.

I thought being an academic was brilliant despite there being lots of frustrations. I really enjoyed communicating with students, teaching them about science, and things that interested me. I enjoyed standing up in front of one person or groups of 100 people.

I was an academic for eight years. After four years at Brunel I lectured for four years at the University of Brighton. During this time I realised that every institution has a slightly different focus on which subjects they specialise in or what their research interests are. At University of Brighton there was a big environmental physiology research group, so I learned lots about exercising in different environmental conditions. At Brunel there had been a slightly different research focus around cardiovascular health. When you're thinking about going to different universities you probably don't realise that departments have a specific research focus as it just seems like a sports science course. But actually if you're really interested in environmental physiology, Brighton is an amazing place to go; if you're really interested in cardiovascular health, Brunel's got some really great people. It is not essential that your interests match the University's interests, but it may help in the future.

Then you moved away from academia into the applied world?

Yes, from there I moved to the English Institute of Sport (EIS) as the head of physiology. That was a big jump and a particularly steep learning curve. I was the first person to come into a head of service role at the EIS from academia rather than through the applied sport system. Academia and the applied world are connected but are so different. As an academic you need a deep expertise of your subject and an ability to convey that information to teach students. As an applied practitioner you must also have technical expertise, but more important is your ability to communicate your knowledge to a wide range of people in order to influence them to adopt your suggestions or to interest them in the data you have collected. In the applied world we also have a performance backwards approach, that is, aligning everything we do to improving performance, whether through the athletes' health, wellbeing, and training, recovery or in-event strategies. This is not always the approach taken in research. However, there are certainly some academics who help support our work by the generation of knowledge and give us insights from what they're researching. These people understand the environment and the constraints that we're working with in high performance sport.

I've been at the EIS for the past five years and while I didn't take the traditional route into this job it has worked out well for me. The more traditional route is that people come into applied sport a bit earlier as a practitioner. They might have done their bachelor's degree and their master's and maybe some teaching, P.E. teaching or even personal training. Then they come to be a practitioner and work their way up, working providing support to sports and then working in leadership roles before getting to head of services or head of department roles.

What are the skills and qualities needed to work in high performance sports?

One of the things that I'm really passionate about is emphasising the need for people to come out of degrees with not just the knowledge of physiology, psychology and biomechanics, as while that's absolutely fundamental, they also need the skills to be a practitioner who can work effectively with other human beings. In high performance sport we work in a really complex environment where you're trying to influence coaches and athletes positively. Ultimately coaches have ownership over the training programme of an athlete, and the coach and athlete work on that together and often have a very special understanding or relationship. Some people believe that they can walk into a sport and then tell coaches and athletes what to do because they've just finished a degree and a master's and they have all this up-to-date knowledge. In reality that just doesn't happen!

The practitioners who can best influence performance are the ones who have skills of excellent communication and really good emotional intelligence. The key thing is knowing when to step forward and share your knowledge and knowing when to sit back and keep quiet, even though you can see that things are going slightly wrong or athletes and coaches are not necessarily doing what you would suggest they do.

The ability to influence people, to pitch ideas and to engage people is so important. You might think that if you're working with other people these are things you'd have but we see so many people walk through the door who are over-confident, arrogant, who aren't willing to be flexible. We also see people who are under-confident and who can't communicate well. No matter how clever or well qualified they are they never thrive and barely last a year. Working in performance sports is quite a high-octane environment and you have to be really flexible as a practitioner to fit into these complex situations. It's not as simple as being able to work with an athlete and tell them what's the best thing to do.

To work in this environment, we want to know that someone has the ability to learn how to act as well as have the basic knowledge. When I say basic knowledge, I mean a degree and master's level knowledge about physiology. But also that they've learnt the skills of problem solving and critical thinking and are able to read academic material and translate it into something that they can apply.

Ultimately, we employ the person with the best set of skills to engage people and to influence and communicate with other people and have empathy. Unfortunately, we see too many graduates come out of their sports science degree thinking they are the bee's knees and that they know everything. When they walk into a new environment, whether it's sport, medical, clinical or personal training, they don't have the humility to accept that that they have to earn their place and know that there are different ways to showcase their knowledge.

If you've done a sports science degree it's very likely that you're going to end up working with another human being, whether it's a patient, a client, a sports person or a coach. There needs to be an emphasis on developing those people skills throughout degrees.

How can students go about developing these skills if they are not developed when they study?

We'll say that whilst you're doing your degree go to a local rugby team or go to your local athletics club and ask, 'can I help you?' 'Can I help you think about how you train your athletes or how athletes recover after a game?' By doing that you will learn how a coach thinks or how to communicate ideas that athletes can engage with and get on board with. You'll learn that actually doing the simple things can be really tricky even before you can share your own ideas. We say, 'go out and earn your bread and butter with anyone who will accept your help'. It tends to be people who have done that who will really shine when they get to us rather than people who have just done their degree, done their master's and only ever done testing and laboratory work. They haven't really had to go out and problem solve in real sporting environments where things tend to be much more complex than in theory. The experience gives them something to talk about and tell us about during an interview.

What about internships, are they a good way for students to develop skills?

Internships are so valuable as students actually expose themselves to the real world and some of our practitioners have come through degree courses where they have a placement year. They have actually had the opportunity to spend a whole year embedded in a role. We have a high proportion of people who get jobs with us who have gone down that route rather than have come straight from a three-year degree. It's their ability to take what you've learned and being able to communicate and apply it, as well as understand the complex environment that is so important. Whether you are at university or working in sport, there's always politics and other things that you don't appreciate until you immerse yourself in an environment and I think learning about that is really valuable. You can do it by volunteering or by doing a placement.

Experience can come in many different ways. We have one member of staff who has risen really quickly through the ranks. After university she set up a dog walking business and while she knew that wasn't what she wanted to do she developed some really important skills. She had to deal with people's precious pets and communicate with them and really make them trust her and believe that she wouldn't harm their dogs. All of those skills, even though they are completely removed from sport, just shine through in her. What she learned during that period helped her in her future career, so people don't necessarily need to get experience from sport. It's really helpful if you do but doing anything that involves dealing with people and the human dimension requires emotional intelligence to keep people happy. She learnt how to deal with conflict and cope in difficult situations and well, that's what your everyday life is like in sport.

Additional resource

Supporting Champions podcast featuring Emma Ross

https://www.supportingchampions.co.uk/podcast/episode/c01009c5/emma-ross-on-the-female-athlete-and-equality-in-performance-cultures

Interview 5

Luke Gupta

Exercise Physiologist and Researcher

Name

Luke Gupta

Job title

Exercise Physiologist at English Institute of Sport

Qualifications

PhD Sleep and athletic performance (Loughborough University)

MSc Exercise Physiology (Loughborough University)

BSc (Hons) Sport and Exercise Science (University of Bath)

Introduction

Luke is an exercise physiologist based at Bisham Abbey. He has a role that involves providing physiological support to athletes from a range of sports combined with research into the relationship between sleep and performance.

Tell me about your job role

I work at the English Institute of Sport at Bisham Abbey and my role is split four ways. The first part is working for the Performance Innovation team who are a research team at the EIS. That role encompasses working with sports on specific projects. Physiologists and nutritionists get assigned to specific sports and work with that sport through an Olympic cycle. We are looking at key themes and common problems in sports and inputting data to present information in different ways to how it is normally done. That is a consultancy type role.

Secondly, I am doing a part-time doctorate funded by EIS into sleep. This is my fifth year and looks at 'Do athletes sleep well and do they know how to manage their sleep?' Athletes are particularly challenged as they have to travel and go to overseas competitions; there is a lot of pressure on them to be successful, so they can maintain funding. As a result, their ability to sleep can come under strain, so I have tried to identify vulnerable sleepers. Most of my work is new and novel because not much work has been previously done in this area. I might look at an individual's sleeping position or what they do before going to bed.

The third part is as an applied physiologist and I work with athletes in sports who don't have an assigned physiologist in their teams. I work on heat acclimation, travel management and whatever a sport needs. I try to answer physiology-based performance questions that will help athletes manage environmental challenges.

Finally, I look after the physiology laboratories at Bisham Abbey in a laboratory technician type role by maintaining equipment and stock.

Tell me about your education

At school I did GCSEs including P.E. and then A-levels in biology, psychology, chemistry and P.E. alongside playing a lot of sport. Because I enjoyed sport and studying science it seemed that sport science would be what I studied at university. I went to Bath University, although I was looking at Loughborough as well. I played hockey and Bath had a National League hockey team so that was the main driving force behind my university selection. I did a four-year sandwich course where in the third-year students get to go on placement to a sport science institution or a professional team.

My placement was at Tottenham Hotspur Football Club which was a great experience. I had an insight into what professional sport was like and what needs to be done to allow sport science to be applied. At the time it didn't always feel like sports science, as my main jobs were mixing recovery carbohydrate and protein shakes for the team and travelling with the team to away matches and cooking pizzas for the players on the bus on the way home. Maybe these jobs weren't sports science, but they were still important jobs that the permanent sports scientist staff didn't have time to do.

I did get an insight into sports science practices that professional clubs use and the challenges sports scientists face on a daily basis working with high profile coaches and players. Also, how the interaction between the sports scientists, the players and the coaches works. I was lucky at Tottenham as the sports science set up was very good. I was the first student to have a placement there and now virtually every football club offers them. I lived with a family for a year away from friends and my own family and had to cycle to the club every day, so it has given me an appreciation of what it feels like to be a placement student living away from home and having to fund yourself which can be difficult in your third year at university. If I hadn't had that experience it would have slowed down my thought process about what I wanted to do as I realised that I wasn't suited to work in professional sport.

Did you stay in education after your undergraduate degree?

Yes, I went to Loughborough University to do a master's degree in Exercise Physiology. I was told by a number of people that to be an exercise physiologist you really needed to have a master's degree. Due to my experience at Tottenham I was able to get a placement with the in-house sports science service at Loughborough University. They do work with student athletes many of which represent GB. They also do external work so other athletes can get lab testing and training support.

This was good for me because I had a license to work with coaches and athletes and develop the different skills like communication and building relationships with people. The master's degree was taught but the focus was very much on you to find things out in contrast to an undergraduate degree where you are given material to learn and then do exams or coursework based on it. At master's level you have to do the extra research to learn about your topic. Due to my work with the sport science service I had the opportunity to do my dissertation with GB swimming. It was applied research and I learnt some key lessons about research.

At this point I thought I was finished with education and it was time to get a job, but I quickly realized there weren't that many jobs. Some of my friends went on to work in universities to continue research and became lecturers, others went to places like Nuffield Health into roles as physiologists. I kept on my role with GB swimming and worked in a coffee shop to keep things ticking over. I had good opportunities with GB swimming such as when the physiologist went on holiday for a month and I stepped in.

During this time, I had about eight unsuccessful interviews, but my experience of interviews grew, and I learnt how to behave in these environments and the types of questions asked. I eventually got an internship at the English Institute of Sport working on talent identification. This was part of a team who ran nationwide campaigns to find the athletes of the future. The initiative was called 'Power 2 Podium' and we put people through screening and identified which sport they may be suited to. This model has been used in Australia and is called talent transfer and it is now used quite widely in the UK. I worked with about 15 placement students and we travelled around the UK for about two months from Scotland to Cardiff. It was good experience on how to manage fitness testing with large groups over a long period of time. There were research projects within that as well. I was also involved working with sports on how they could identify talent and develop them into athletes with a chance of winning a medal.

After this I went to work with the EIS physiology team as a laboratory technician working with staff from British Cycling and UK Athletics. At this point I was made aware that an opportunity for a PhD was coming up to amalgamate the laboratory technician role with a research role. I interviewed for that successfully and have been doing it for five years now.

Can you summarise the role of the exercise physiologist?

The role of the exercise physiologist is to understand how athletes respond to training and design novel interventions to allow them to realize their physiological potential. Physiological demands are very different between sports; for example, some endurance sports use lots of high-volume training and monitoring of physiological responses is very important. Coaches put them through rigorous training programs in comparison to boxing where the main aim is to knock your opponent out. The challenge of the physiologist is changing coaches' perceptions of what training looks like. In some endurance sports the coaches generally believe in the philosophy of 'the more training the better'. The physiologist needs to work closely with a coach and get an insight into their thinking and try to challenge that and maybe find ways to change or improve training. This can be difficult if you have a coach responsible for multiple gold medals and you are telling them to change as they will question why they should change what works.

What is the importance of soft skills in your role and what are they?

There was a time when an employer looked for the most qualified person on paper thinking that the softer skills would be developed along the way. Now it is almost the other way as employers look for good people who will fit in with their culture knowing they can teach them the technical skills. Working with people is about getting on with them and while good communication and good listening are important if you can get on with the coach and the athletes in a sport you are going to be successful.

If you get on with the coach, you will be able to have more conversations and get more insight into their world and how they tick just by spending time with them. If you don't get on with them, they can become closed off, so you don't get the insight you need to create change.

I am quite introverted which is a trait considered not to be appropriate for work in elite sport. There was a time where the louder you shouted the more you got noticed. For example, in interviews when there were group tasks the more confident, extraverted people came to the fore and got taken on. Whereas now there seems to be a better appreciation of different personality types and there is not only one personality type that fits the role of the physiologist. You need to have different types of people in a team to make it function. My personal qualities are listening and thinking. These can be a downfall as I can be too busy listening that I may not say anything, and I can get lost in my thoughts. The benefit of these skills in a team is that you have a person who really listens whereas a lot of people say they are listening, but they are really thinking about the next question or they will miss something. They may lack flexibility to let a conservation go somewhere that they had not planned for it to go. I can work with most sports as I can get on with people and listen to the questions they have and what their concerns are and then deliver a solution. I can reflect on what I have done and about how I could change it to work in different situations.

What advice would you give students who wanted a similar career to yours?

Perseverance is important because the job you want may not come overnight. When you finish your degree and have some experience it may or may not be enough. You need to be aware that you may have to go through the process of applying for jobs, failing, learning and then going again. Elite sport is highly competitive and attractive, and you do get people who are overqualified going for jobs. Be aware that you may not succeed on your first attempt and it is okay to feel that you are being rejected for no apparent reason other than there was someone slightly more suited to the job than you.

Try and find a niche for yourself. My niche is that I have flexibility, so I can work in lots of different sports and understand the culture quickly. Also, sleep is a niche subject. Even doctorates are quite common in sport and having a doctorate is no longer a niche if you want to be a physiologist. A niche is somewhere that you, as a person, can make a difference. It is important to have technical expertise and the ability to apply what you learn on your degree but the real lesson you pick up with experience is that success is based on how you interact with people and shape your personality to the situation.

There is no one personality type that makes a successful physiologist. If you know yourself, your strengths, where you want to go and show perseverance then you will eventually get there.

Are there parts of your job that you don't enjoy or like less?

In my role I have to travel a lot and may have to get on a train or in the car at 5 am to go to Nottingham or Lilleshall and the travelling is challenging. While it's good to get out of the office and see different people I do feel jealous of people who go to the same place every day. Sometimes it feels like I have done nothing except seen someone for an hour and spent the rest of the time travelling. However, there is so much value in speaking to people face to face that it is worth it, and people do appreciate it.

There are challenges from the different ways that people in different sports work. You can feel you are banging your head against a brick wall when you try to implement change, or you make a change that doesn't work. It can be frustrating when people don't see things the way you do so you need to get into their shoes and see things from their perspective.

To be brutally honest it is not particularly well paid. Olympic sports are government funded so we don't earn the salaries that they may do in professional football or rugby. If money was your driving force, you would work in professional sport. For people who work supporting Olympic sports money cannot be the driving factor. You need intrinsic motivation and supporting athletes in the next best thing to being an elite athlete yourself. I enjoy helping others achieve their goals and take rewards from that.

Interview 6

Will Abbott

Strength and Conditioning Coach

Name

Will Abbott

Job title

Head of Strength and Conditioning and Sports Science at Brighton and Hove Albion Football Club Academy

Qualifications

MSc in Sports Performance, Portsmouth University

BSc (Hons) Sport and Exercise Science, Portsmouth University

Introduction

Will is head of the strength and conditioning and sport science department for the Academy at Brighton and Hove Albion Football Club. The Academy consists of age group teams from under-9s all the way up to under-23s and he is responsible for all these age groups.

What does a strength and conditioning coach do?

A strength and conditioning coach will prescribe an exercise programme specific to improving the performance of an athlete in competition. In order to do this, they have to be fully aware of the movement demands and physical requirements of a sport and the different roles within a sport. As well as improving performance they will work to prevent athletes becoming injured.

Strength and conditioning are not just about weight training to improve strength and power but will involve a range of training methods, such as plyometrics, flexibility training, core strength training, speed and agility and endurance training. In particular strength and conditioning coaches will look at an athletes' technique and movement patterns to assess whether they moving as effectively as they can. If they are moving inefficiently, they may be expending excess energy or setting themselves up to become injured. The strength and conditioning coach may have to prescribe a flexibility routine to release tension in certain muscle groups and allow joints to move more freely or have a greater range of motion.

Tell me about your education

I did A-levels in Holland in a British school as my parents were based there. I did biology, geography, P.E. and German and then got a place at Portsmouth University. I did a degree in sport and exercise science which took three years. During my final year I saw an advertisement for an internship at Southampton Football Club which involved spending 1-

2 days a week at the club gaining experience doing the fundamental tasks of a sport scientist. This gave me experience about what strength and conditioning was really about. I needed this as I had no knowledge apart from the modules I studied on my degree.

This lit the fire within me and was my first foray into strength and conditioning. I had an idea about the route I wanted to go down, so I stayed at Portsmouth to complete a Master's degree (MSc) in Sport Performance. Most master's courses specialize in one area such as biomechanics, psychology or strength and conditioning but this MSc was like the undergraduate degree but in more detail. There were modules in physiology, psychology, biomechanics and strength and conditioning and nutrition but in more depth so giving me a good breadth of understanding. The reason it appealed to me was that at this point I wasn't entirely sure which route I wanted to go down and I wanted to keep my options open. I had one or two different interests and things I wanted to learn about rather than pigeonhole myself in a certain discipline at an early stage. I continued the internship at Southampton during my master's year for a second season and this was important to me that I could get applied experience alongside my master's. At the end of that year I had two years applied experience and a master's degree.

How has the breadth of sports science knowledge that you gained helped with your work as a Strength and Conditioning Coach?

It has been important in my current role working within the Academy, but I think that the further you get into your career then the more specialised you become. However, due to the shortage of staff in the Academy we are often forced to become a generalist and have a reasonable level of understanding in a number of different subject areas.

Have you had to take additional courses in strength and conditioning for your current role?

Yes, one of the main qualifications employers require is the UK Strength and Conditioning Association (UKSCA) accreditation. It is the strength and conditioning accreditation for the UK and the qualification that football clubs and other sports teams looking for strength and conditioning coaches require. It is stated as a requirement on most strength and conditioning job descriptions – either to have the UKSCA qualification or be on the way to achieving it. For example, the job description may say to have the ability to achieve the qualification within a six-month period.

Are there different levels in the UKSCA?

No, there is just one level that is seen as the minimum standard to be deemed a safe and knowledgeable strength and conditioning coach – you are either accredited or you are not.

How long did it take you to achieve?

There are four workshops that you have to go on before you sit your exam. A weightlifting workshop, a speed, agility and plyometrics workshop, a case study and a beginners' course that is recommended if you are at the start of your career. Then you prepare for your examination which is in four parts. There are two practical parts and two theory parts. From my experience and other people's, they are not easy exams to pass first time; it has taken me about two years from attending my first workshop to passing the final exam. It is a significant undertaking, but some master's degrees do prepare you for the accreditation, such as at Middlesex and St Mary's Universities they have modules to help fast track you towards the accreditation. People studying those courses may pass in one or two attempts but for most people it can take three or four attempts. It is not an accreditation that can be gained in a couple of months.

Can you tell about your current role and what your job entails?

As head of the strength and conditioning department I manage a small team of coaches and sports scientists. We have five staff in total and from a management perspective I oversee all the strength and conditioning and sport science support we provide for the academy athletes. I set the blueprint and the philosophy for the department and manage the coaches and sport scientists within the department to carry out the blueprint. I'll conduct their annual reviews and deal with any issues that they have and develop them as coaches by organising CPD (continuing professional development) and their development in their careers. Alongside the management role I am very hands on as a practitioner. I have to be because of our low staffing levels and the high number of athletes that we have I don't have the luxury of sitting back and being the manager. But I really enjoy the practical side of it, and it is an important part of my role as I still have a lot of developing to do.

From a practitioner perspective I work with the under-23 players on a daily basis leading their gym and pitch-based conditioning to ensure they are at their physical best when they are competing, and that they stay as fit and healthy as possible and avoid injury. I provide additional sports science support through monitoring training load and using GPS tracking and advising on nutrition. I also run workshops on recovery and how players can manage their bodies over a long, arduous season.

What does a strength and conditioning coach do across the season?

In pre-season, one of our main roles is to fitness test the players, so they'll go through a battery of tests to see where they are and whether they have been adhering to their training programmes during the off-season. This involves endurance, power, speed and strength tests and we feed information back to the medical staff and pass on our recommendations. We might highlight a few individuals who are at risk of injury because they are not at the same fitness level as the others and pass that on to the coaches.

During the pre-season, and during the competitive season we work very closely with the coaching staff planning what players will do on a daily basis. We meet in the morning and discuss which players they have available and what we recommend they should be doing on that day to meet their physical aims. We tie it in with the work coaches want them to do on their technical skills. Technical skills are the most important as the players must be good at playing football. Being fit is a secondary characteristic to players' technical skills.

We then go out onto the pitch and lead the warm up before the coach's training session and prepare the athletes for the training that is coming to reduce the likelihood of injury. We lead all the gym-based training which may be two or three sessions a week depending on the stage of the season. We lead various sessions, such as upper or lower body sessions, sessions focusing on power or strength. We'll design the sessions based on our yearly plan which has been broken down into monthly, weekly and daily plans. We have to structure gym based and pitch-based work throughout the season and make sure we are doing the right amount of work on the right days. For example, not doing too much work before a game so that they ae not fatigued during it.

These periodized programmes apply sports science principles but probably 90% of the time we are forced to adapt our plans. This may be because they don't marry up with what the coach wants or something changes, such as a fixture gets moved or a player isn't in the shape or at the level you expect them to be. So, it's all and well having plans, but we must be very adaptable to what is in front of us.

Being adaptable and doing it with good humour and good grace seems to be a key skill. Are there any other qualities that are important in being an effective strength and conditioning coach?

I'd say the ability to communicate at all different levels. We work as a multidisciplinary team and as part of that team we have physiotherapists who are very well educated and qualified. We work with football coaches who may have sports science degrees or sports coaching degrees and also players at different levels of maturity and intelligence. You might be working with under-10s one day and under-23s the next and have to adapt how you get your message across and structure your feedback. It will be very different for a younger athlete compared to an older athlete. You may speak very differently to a member of medical staff to when you are talking to a coach. There may be differences when you talk to a coach who is an ex-player to one who has done a sports science degree. The ability to pitch your message across to different members of staff is a skill in itself.

Your ability to manage your emotions is very important. There are going to be bad days when the club lose games of football and there will be fantastic days when you win. It is important to not become too emotionally involved in the little things that affect you doing your job to the best of your ability, like getting into an argument or focusing on the negatives and letting that affect your performance. If you have played sport yourself, you know how emotions can affect you and it's the same if you are a member of staff. If your team loses a game, it is very easy to get caught up in the emotion but it's important to see the bigger picture and focus on the long term.

These are things a degree doesn't necessarily prepare you for and only by being in elite sport environments for a period of time will you be prepared. It's a difficult thing to teach in a structured degree so when I get students messaging me for career advice I always say, 'go out and get as much experience as you can with people and working with athletes as possible.' It really doesn't need to be working with elite athletes or athletes at all. It could be at the gym working as a gym instructor with the general population and listening to their issues. You may have the opportunity to work with a 40-year old female for a session followed by a 20-year old male and have to communicate and work in completely different ways with both. Only by getting out and experiencing these situations can you be prepared in any way.

You can only learn through experiences and reflecting on these experiences.

Are there any drawbacks or parts of your job that you enjoy less?

Potentially a drawback is the number of hours that you have to work in football, and you have to understand this before you choose to work in professional sport. The hours are typically anti-social as sport is played at weekends and in the evenings. Particularly with the younger age groups who are still at school the work will be in the evenings. You do have to make sacrifices from a social perspective, such as weddings and weekends away missed. I think the majority of people who work in sport do so not because it is the best paid job but because they have a passion for sport, and they are or were sportspeople themselves. The next best thing to being an athlete is to work with and support an athlete's career. People are willing to make sacrifices because they have a passion for what they are doing.

There are some fantastic moments when I think this is why I work in football. But there can be other moments, such as when you are on the team bus coming back from Newcastle or the Midlands, the team have lost 3-0 and you have to get up in 5 hours' time and you think 'why I am doing this when I could be doing something else'. But there are more days when I come away thinking it is fantastic to be working in sports science and strength and conditioning.

What about the future – what would you see as being your next move?

I am currently just finishing my doctorate at University of Brighton focusing on the role of the use of GPS as a training load monitoring tool. This combines my work at the football club with research at the university. Once I have that qualification it may open up more doors for me to transition to in the future.

There are three potential routes. Firstly, moving up to the first team and working as a strength and conditioning coach. Secondly, a position becoming more popular is a head of performance role. We have lots of smaller teams, such as strength and conditioning, sports science, physiotherapy, sports analysts, sport psychologists and nutritionists. There is often a person put in place to oversee the work of all those teams and ensure they are working together as effectively as possible rather than operating individually. That person is the head of performance and it is a pure management role. They ensure the right structures are in place within the various departments to enable them to work with one another as effectively as possible. Thirdly, there is research and academia. Having studied for my doctorate I've had a few things published and spoken at conferences and it is something I would like to continue in the future. Having said that there are still several things I want to achieve in elite sport but there may come a time when working the anti-social hours in elite sport become less friendly to the family environment. This may be a young person's game and there may come a time when it appeals less to me. The doctorate allows me to potentially go down that route. I am very happy in this role and still have many goals I want to achieve but the doctorate may open a few doors further down the line.

Would you say there are many opportunities for strength and conditioning coaches across the country or is it still tough to get into?

It's an area that is growing quickly. When I think back to when I was graduating and I was always checking online websites, such UKSCA, UK Sport and BASES every day and you were lucky if one job came up a week. There are many more jobs coming up now because of the increase in the number of staff working in football academies. There are many more opportunities for strength and conditioning coaches and sport scientists in football purely because of the Premier League's stipulations. There are more opportunities in rugby union who are looking at football and how it is structured in terms of staffing levels. There are more opportunities in schools as well, particularly those schools that take sport seriously and offer sports scholarships. Universities employ strength and conditioning coaches to work with their sports teams, again particularly those universities who take sport very seriously. There are more opportunities becoming available but the pool of people graduating with strength and conditioning degrees and sport science degrees has increased with most universities offering sports degrees of some sort. There are more jobs but also more people looking for jobs.

Additional resource

UK Strength and Conditioning Association

https://www.uksca.org.uk/

Interview 7

Laura Heathcote

Physiotherapist

Name

Laura Heathcote

Job title

Physiotherapist for Great Britain Women's Wheelchair Basketball team

Qualifications

BSc (Hons) Physiotherapy, Sheffield Hallam University

MSc Advanced Manipulative Physiotherapy, University of Birmingham

Introduction

Laura is the physiotherapist for the Great Britain Women's Wheelchair Basketball team who won the silver medal at the 2018 World Championships. This was their first podium finish at a senior championship, and she is currently preparing the team for the 2020 Paralympic Games in Tokyo.

What does your job entail?

My job is to minimise the impact of illness and injury and make sure our athletes are available for as much time as possible as this ultimately impacts on performance. On a weekly basis it changes all the time, and this keeps me interested and engaged. My daily work depends on the players' schedule. The players train every day on court and have two to three strength and conditioning sessions a week as well. I tend to be around when the girls are on court in case there are any injuries and I attend the strength and conditioning sessions if I can. I work very closely with the strength and conditioning coach to maximise certain individuals' performance in those sessions. Because they all have different impairments it can be helpful for the strength and conditioning coach and myself to look at how we might position an athlete to complete an exercise or how we might modify the exercise to get the adaptation we need and target specific muscle groups.

I have set weekly physiotherapy clinic times in my diary that players can book to get treatment for injuries and rehabilitation. From an injury point of view, we don't tend to see too many serious injuries. Most injuries are small niggles that I need to treat and put strategies in place to prevent them from reoccurring. I will work with the coaches and the strength and conditioning coach to look at athlete training load and how we deliver that training. If we find big spikes or troughs in training load that are producing injuries, we need to find a way to mitigate for this and plan our workload more effectively to minimise the risk of injuries. Injuries will impact availability of athletes which in turn impacts on performance.

All the practitioners who form the multidisciplinary team that work the players meet once a week. Within our wheelchair basketball programme this multidisciplinary team is made up of me as physiotherapist for the women's team, the physiotherapist for the men's team, a part-time nutritionist, part-time sport psychologist, a performance analyst, a strength and conditioning coach and a performance lifestyle coach. We meet to discuss concerns that we have about certain athletes' illnesses and injuries and any other concerns we have.

I also meet with the strength and conditioning coach and the team's coaches once a week to look at athlete training load and discuss the training week ahead. We discuss if we need to modify anything for specific athletes due to illness, injury or any reason an athlete may not be available due to other commitments, such as university studies. We also plan what the year looks like with regard to competition, time off and time playing away and ensure sufficient recovery time is planned within the schedule. We give the plan back to the athletes so they can visualise what their year looks like and it helps to manage their expectations and keep them focused on their end goal.

I travel with the squad to tournaments and also with the junior women's team's tournaments as long as it doesn't disrupt my work with the senior team. For example, this summer (2019) I will travel to Thailand with the junior team for their World Championship and then to Holland with the senior team for their European Championships.

Within our programme we run research projects such as a recent one we did on jet lag. The next Paralympic Games are going to be in Tokyo and the impact of jet lag can be massive and could limit player availability for training when they first get to Japan. We need to have strategies in place to maximise player availability and minimise the impact of jet lag on athlete wellbeing and performance.

Tell me about your education

I always knew that I wanted to be a physiotherapist, so I mapped out the education I needed to do to get there. I did four AS levels in chemistry, human biology, psychology and sports studies. At A2 level I dropped chemistry and kept on with the other three subjects. I chose human biology as it was an entry requirement to have biology or human biology to study physiotherapy at university.

I did my undergraduate degree at Sheffield Hallam University and graduated in 2010 with a BSc (Hons) in Physiotherapy. Once I had finished my degree I worked as a junior physiotherapist in the National Health Service (NHS) and after about five years a vacancy came up at the English Institute of Sport for a funded master's degree at Birmingham

University. I did my Master's degree in Advanced Manipulative Physiotherapy alongside an internship programme working with Paralympic sports. I got advanced education from the master's programme and an in depth understanding of the musculoskeletal system combined with practical exposure to working with athletes in a number of different Paralympic sports. At this point I left my job in the NHS and went to work in Paralympic sport. Sport is always where I wanted to end up as I've always been passionate about it. When I finished my master's degree a job came up with British Wheelchair Basketball Association at the English Institute of Sport in Sheffield, so that's how I ended up in my current role.

When you do a physiotherapy degree, how much content is sport focused?

When I was applying for physiotherapy degrees the most important piece of advice I was given was do not put on your personal statement that you want to work in sport. This is because it is not looked favourably upon and gives the opinion that you may have already narrowed your career choices. From a physiotherapy point of view only about 5% of physiotherapists work in sport and there is a huge world out there of physiotherapy that is not sport related. For five years after my degree I did junior rotations working in intensive care, mental health, general surgery and respiratory wards. There are so many aspects to physiotherapy that are not sport related that if you want to go into a physiotherapy degree wanting to be a sports physiotherapist and neglecting the rest it won't be looked on favourably. It doesn't mean you won't become a sports physiotherapist if that is your goal, but you should remember that it won't be the sole focus of your degree studies.

The work I did on amputee wards, working in intensive care and the other rotations I did made me a more rounded physiotherapist when I wanted to specialise in sport. If I have an athlete who has an asthma attack, I have a knowledge base from which to work from because I did a respiratory placement. I might have an athlete who is visually impaired or blind but that's fine because some my patients in the NHS were blind and I had to adapt my style to work with them. It gives you a wealth of experience if you go straight from an undergraduate degree into sport you can lose a miss out on developing your broader skill set.

Those placements made me who I am now by exposing me to new experiences and I wouldn't be the practitioner I am now if I didn't have that wide experience. If you go to a physiotherapy interview or write your personal statement without considering this broader world of physiotherapy the chances are that you won't get on the course.

In terms of getting experience before you apply for a physiotherapy degree if you've got experience of a sport environment then that's fine but if you can get into a hospital and see what physiotherapy really is then it will put you in a much better position. A lot of people think about physiotherapy being about sport, but it is such a small part of it. You could end up in an intensive care ward and realise that physiotherapy is not necessarily what you though it was. Getting experience is critical to understanding physiotherapy.

At the end of a physiotherapy degree you may come out and say 'I still want to work in sport' but these wider skills are still necessary.

Do you need a master's degree as well to be an effective sports physiotherapist?

No you don't need one and it's not essential, but I would say it is desirable and helpful. When I did my master's degree I knew I wanted to specialise in musculoskeletal physiotherapy in sport and Paralympic sport; it enabled me to refine and build on what I had learnt in my undergraduate degree. I wanted to challenge my clinical reasoning process which is why I assess what I assess and treat what I treat so I can refine the process and be really specific in treatments. It was particularly useful to do the master's after working for five years and really reflect on what I was doing and how I treat people.

Why did you want to work in sport and in particular in disability sports?

I've always loved sport and was on every team in school, the basketball team, the athletics team and was a competitive athlete for a number of years. I loved being active and doing sport. I always knew I wanted to work with a group of interesting people and was interested in the disability side of things. When I was a junior physiotherapist in the NHS one of my rotations was working on a surgical ward. This involved amputee rehabilitation and that opened my eyes to working with amputees. I was also working in the amputee rehabilitation centre at the time, teaching young amputees how to walk again and function. I loved it and when a vacancy came up working with amputees I jumped at the chance and got to do that for 12 months. At the time I was also working with lower limb rehabilitation, such as anterior cruciate ligament (ACL) reconstruction, so it was the best of both worlds for me. I also had a friend who went to fight in the war in Afghanistan and he was injured and came back with his leg amputated. This sparked my interest further so that I could do something to help him.

I also became a classifier for British Athletics working to classify athletes relative to their impairment. This opened my eyes to different impairments such as visual impaired athletes and physically impaired athletes. When I did my masters in 2015, I already had a number of years' experience in amputee rehabilitation and athlete classification, so I knew that disability sport was where I wanted to end up working as it combined my interests in Paralympic sport, physiotherapy and elite sport.

What are the main challenges working in elite or performance sport?

One of the big challenges that is specific to working in Paralympic sports is that no two athletes are ever the same and each person truly is an individual. The challenge is trying to rehab an athlete when there are no guidelines on how to do it. If you have to rehab a footballer's ACL injury then you can open a book and find out, but there is nothing on rehab for a quadriplegic cerebral palsy athlete. You have to be really creative as you might be the first to try something out because no one else has seen that specific injury in that specific impairment group before. You are always having to think outside the box and about the way you are doing something. The way you might treat an injury in an able-bodied athlete may not be appropriate for a disabled athlete.

How do you develop the trust of your athletes to enable you to treat them?

The best skills that people working in physiotherapy can have is the ability to build relationships, rapport and trust with someone. This is critical as you can be the best physiotherapist in the world with the best rehabilitation plans but if your athletes don't do the rehab work you have asked them to do then it becomes irrelevant. If they don't trust you or your work, then they won't do their rehab. My skills come from working with different people and the experience I have had with the NHS, sports teams and British Athletics. It's about working with a wide range of people and having the ability to communicate with them.

Athletes and coaches have to trust you. If I say that I need to take an athlete out of training or trial this treatment with them they will say; 'how do I know this is going to work'. Unfortunately, the research or the literature may not be there, so I have to back it up and justify why we have to try this, and they have to trust your judgement. This may come from working with them over a number of years and they learn to trust you and the decisions you make.

The ability to build relationships and influence people at different levels is really crucial. Being good at the basics of your job is important as you can do rehab that looks brilliant but if it's not targeting what it needs to target it doesn't matter what it looks like. You need to do the basics and do them right.

What other skills and qualities do you need to work in high performance sports?

Building relationships and rapport is the number one priority, especially when working as part of a multidisciplinary team. You can't get away with being a silent practitioner and you find that in performance sport most practitioners are pretty passionate. It's about being able to work with people who want to do something totally different to you and being able to be flexible and meet in the middle to get what is best for that athlete. You need to be able to build relationships with people and within a group of people so you can have influence.

Being creative is really crucial because for us it is about thinking about that athlete in front of you and how you might rehab them. We might see the same injury, but it is in two athletes with different disabilities then they will present completely differently. The best rehab exercises for us are not written in a book or found online. Sometimes they may not be able to get in a certain position or do an exercise so the ability to be creative and come up with individual solutions is crucial. Also, athletes get bored if you give them the same exercises all the time. They challenge us as much as we challenge them to be creative.

Being able to write a rehab plan that works backwards from an athlete's end goal to where they are now is important. It is a skill but it's an art as well and is about looking at what their performance looks like and working back from there within the time frame you may have. You may only have a limited amount of time and so you need to be really specific and creative in your approach.

What advice would you give a young person who wanted to work as a physiotherapist?

You need to go out of your way to find volunteer work and get some experience. You can't expect it to find you and you won't get anything that you haven't worked hard for. You can't expect to graduate and go to a sports team and hope to get work if you haven't had experience. You will have to go out of your way and do things for free. A lot of people want to work in sport, so you have to work out what will make you stand out from the crowd. For example, when I had just qualified I volunteered with a basketball team and the work I had done with British Athletics stood me in good stead when I came to apply and interview for the job as it is experience that people want. People need to see what you can do as well as what you know. If an opportunity comes your way that helps you to get where you want to go grab it with both hands before someone else does. But be specific and don't just say 'yes' to everything because if your end goal is to work in elite Paralympic sports you can't say yes to things that don't help with that goal as you may lose time doing something less relevant.

Networking is important so it's useful to attend conferences and talk to people working in that field. Don't be afraid to ask people questions and ask if you can see what they do, why and how they do it

Work hard and don't give up. You might not get that job, but you might get the next one. Getting into sport is tough so you've got to work hard and not give in.

Which parts of your job do you most enjoy, and which parts do you enjoy less?

The best part for me is being able to rehabilitate an athlete back to performance following an injury. Physiotherapists become physiotherapists so that they can get injured people back to doing something that they currently cannot. Also, working in Paralympic sports I get to be really creative with rehabilitation plans and am not confined to following set protocols.

I enjoy being involved with projects that will impact performance at the highest level and maximise athlete availability at the highest level. I like being able to work with likeminded individuals in a multidisciplinary team who enjoy working with a unique group of athletes and people who like challenges that are not typical or found in textbooks.

Being courtside during a tournament is magical and there are not many sports where you get to be so close to the action. We do what we do to enable them to perform, so to be able to sit courtside and be there with them is a real thrill.

The parts I dislike are when I have to sit at a desk and do administration. Sometimes we have to deliver bad news to an athlete when you know that they won't be able to make a certain event due to the nature of their illness or injury then that is always a hard thing to do.

This final one is specific to Paralympic sports as when we travel it can be a logistical nightmare and I find it quite stressful. We will travel with 12 athletes who each have a wheelchair and a game chair, so that makes 24 wheelchairs. It can be tricky depending on the airline and the destination. When we travel there are certain things that you have to consider that an able-bodied team wouldn't even think about, such as how you will get your athletes on and off the flight as efficiently as possible, or how to get them to the toilet during the flight.

Additional information

Typical university entry requirements for Physiotherapy

Students will need to study three A-levels including either biology, human biology or physical education to gain an offer for physiotherapy. Often universities specify that these need to be achieved at grade A and offers are usually AAB or ABB. Alternatively, a BTEC National Extended Diploma in Sport and Exercise Sciences is also accepted by universities and most offers are for a DDM profile with 128 UCAS tariff points. GCSEs (or equivalent) in Science, Mathematics and sometimes English are also required for entry.

The information here represents typical offers from universities but as offers from universities vary it is vital to research what grades are needed for a successful UCAS application to a university.

Interview 8

Charlotte Haffenden-Gale

Lecturer in Higher Education

Name

Charlotte Haffenden-Gale

Job title

Sports lecturer

Qualifications

MSc Exercise Physiology, Loughborough University

BSc (Hons) Sport and Exercise Science, University of Bath

Post Graduate Certificate in Education, University of Southampton

Introduction

Charlotte lectures on the Foundation Degree in Sports Studies at West Herts College. She also has part-time roles as an Associate Lecturer for The Open University on their BSc (Hons) Sport and Fitness programme and an External Examiner at Easton and Otley College.

How did you get into the position you are in today?

At school I did A-levels in P.E., psychology and maths and then went to Exeter University and completed a BSc (Hons) in Sport and Exercise Science. Once I had completed it I had no idea what to do so I went to work at a private school as an assistant P.E. teacher for a year. I loved it but also realised that I didn't want to work with young age groups, mainly because I wouldn't be using what I learnt on my degree enough.

At this point I decided to do a Post Graduate Certificate in Education (PGCE) at Southampton University so I could teach PE at secondary school level. As part of the course I went on a six-week placement at a sixth form college and loved the experience. I enjoyed working with the 16+ age group and in particular the lecturing side as I felt I was using the knowledge from my degree. After my PGCE I got a job at a college in Southampton as a sport and PE lecturer but also a basketball academy coach. I worked there for two years teaching BTEC Levels 1, 2 and 3 as well as A-Level P.E. At this time, I was also allowed to go and teach at a school and get my qualified teacher status (QTS) which was really important to me as it completed my teacher training.

After teaching for two years, for personal reasons I relocated and came out of teaching. At this point I set myself up as a freelance personal trainer, using the qualification I had gained while I was at University. I worked in the gym at the Stoke Mandeville Stadium and gained clients through a company called Bodywise. I worked in the gym where I was the only personal trainer and the deal with Bodywise was that I made a weekly payment to them related to the number of sessions I was taking a week. I kept the money I made over and above the weekly payment to Bodywise.

After a year I was at the stage where I needed to get into secure employment, so I could get a mortgage, so I could buy a house, and went to work at West Herts College, Watford in 2005. Initially I worked a sports lecturer alongside my personal training business and basketball coaching. After two years it became too much work for me, so I decided to concentrate on lecturing and basketball coaching. At the college I worked in a number of different roles as sports lecturer, then senior lecturer where in addition to teaching I had to support and offer guidance to new staff.

Then the programme manager's role for the Foundation degree came up and I successfully applied for it. The Foundation degree in sports studies is linked to the University of Hertfordshire and it was through the university that I got an external examiner role. This is where I am involved in assessing the quality of provision and assessment of other degree programmes.

In 2011 I applied to work as an associate lecturer for The Open University and was successful to work on the BSc (Hons) Sport and Fitness programme on a part time basis. This involves running tutorials, offering guidance and assessing student work. It is quite flexible and I can fit the work in around my full-time role.

Can you describe what your job as programme manager involves?

I manage a team of lecturers who work on the Foundation degree and ensure they plan their schedule of lectures each year, complete their marking on time, respond to feedback from the external examiner and attend professional development events. A key part of this role is collaborating with our partner, Oaklands College, to deliver the programme and ensure that we plan and prepare together.

I also have a lecturing role and prepare students are ready for their assessments Once they have completed their work I download and mark their assignments. The average contact hours for a lecturer are 23 hours a week, not including marking and planning time but mine is slightly less, so I can fulfil my management role. All lecturers also have a pastoral role supporting students and checking on their progress and wellbeing. That side of the job is evidence based so we have to make records of meetings, phone calls and emails so that we have evidence if a student needs more support.

What did your role at Bodywise in Stoke Mandeville involve?

Bodywise had a relationship with the gym at Stoke Mandeville and once I had agreed to work with Bodywise they placed me at Stoke Mandeville which is one of many gyms that they supply personal trainers to. I was effectively self-employed but made a weekly payment, or rent, to work at the gym and this rent was paid to Bodywise. As personal trainers we were paid by our clients to train them for an hour and we could take as many or as few PT sessions as we wanted. The gym benefitted because while they employed gym instructors, as personal trainers we had a bit more experience and expertise and were able to share it with them. Personal trainers are qualified to a higher standard and generally work exclusively with their own clients rather than working with lots of different clients at a gym. Gym instructors will do fitness assessments and then induct their clients but after that the client trains alone. As a personal trainer we will train our clients two to three times a week.

Bodywise supported our professional development and trained us on how to promote your business, develop our customer base and how to make our business successful. I think it was a good deal because at the beginning we had six weeks where we didn't pay anything to get us going and allow us build up our customer base. Then we started paying incremental amounts of rent up to £100 a week and we took the rest of the money as our income.

Do you think being a lecturer has helped develop your personal skills?

Yes, definitely. For example, recently I did an assertiveness training course and as a result am a bit tougher than I was and less sensitive. I am able to rationalise and understand things that happen better. Lecturing has also helped in terms of my time management and I used to be a perfectionist. Teaching has taught me this is not physically possible to be perfect all the time and sometimes you just have to hit the deadline and that is okay. This has helped me with my children as with children things are not perfect and they never can be. I realise now that sometimes things have to be done and they may be a bit ragged around the edges but that is okay. Lecturing has helped with my communication skills as when teaching you have to learn that there are different ways to communicate with different people and communicate with students who are at different levels; for example, I teach in a different way to degree level students than I do to those studying our BTEC courses.

What advice would you have for a student who wanted to be a sports lecturer?

I would say that you need to be a 'yes' person meaning that when opportunities arise say 'yes' and go for it. Never think that you haven't got time or space to do something if you are offered an opportunity as you never know what is going to come off the back of that. Also, get as much experience in education environments as you can. I had a year teaching in a private school and while it was not what I ultimately wanted to do I learnt so much.

You have to appreciate that nothing lasts forever, but when you get an opportunity you will learn new skills and it can create networking opportunities that you might be able to use in the future.

If you are waiting for something you really want to come along it is beneficial to do something rather than just wait for your dream job. Experiences can act as stepping stones to get to somewhere else so be open minded and embrace all experiences. You must keep searching for opportunities that will help get you where you want to be in the long term.

People talk about getting lucky breaks, but you have to be in a position where you can get a lucky break that you can benefit from.

What do you most enjoy about your job?

I most enjoy teaching the students and working with them in the classroom. Being in the classroom is always the best time for me. I love it when students have that lightbulb moment and you see something clicking for them and their eyes lighten up. That is a great feeling to have.

Any parts of your job that you enjoy less?

Yes, there is a lot of paperwork such as having to track students and gather the evidence you need to get support for a student. It often feels like a pen pushing exercise to me. I think I dislike it because it can feel disrespectful to me as a person as if I am being questioned over whether I am telling the truth.

I also don't enjoy dealing with difficult students and have been in situations where I haven't wanted to teach a group because a student has been so disrespectful to me. It is something that you learn to deal with and get better at over time.

These are minor things and I do find being a lecturer a hugely fulfilling career.

Interview 9

Adam Folwell

PE Teacher

Name

Adam Folwell

Job title

Physical Education Teacher

Qualifications

BA (Hons) Physical Education with QTS (Secondary) University of Bedfordshire

Introduction:

Adam is a PE teacher in at Christopher Hatton Academy and deputy head of the department. He is responsible for delivering lessons in the classroom and in practical sports. He also has responsibility for a year group to ensure their progression and wellbeing. Adam also works as Lead Examiner for an examining board setting exam papers and leading a group of examiners through the marking process.

And how did you get to the position that you're in today?

I did A-levels, but I failed them as I didn't go to school very often. By age 19 I was working in a car auction as my part-time job had become my full-time job. At this point I needed to sort myself out, so I joined the Navy. I did three years in the Royal Navy learning to be a marine engineer. After four years I decided I didn't really want to be an engineer and that I wanted to be a PE teacher.

As I had no qualifications I decided I was going to do an access course to get to university but first I needed to get some work experience. I played cricket with someone who was Head of PE at a school and he let me come and do some work experience. I went to the school for one afternoon a week over a 12-week period and then signed up for an access course. However, that summer I thought I'd chance my arm to get a university place through clearing without completing an access course. After an interview I got a place on a PE teaching degree at University of Bedfordshire, as a mature student. This is not a traditional route and I was lucky to get another chance. I wouldn't recommend it!

What is the traditional route into PE teaching?

After studying A-levels or a BTEC course you go to university and there are a couple of routes. You can do what I did which is a PE degree with Qualified Teacher Status (QTS). It's a four-year course with teaching placements every year. It qualifies you to teach PE in a secondary school. Or you can do a three-year degree in movement studies or sports science and then a one-year Post Graduate Certificate in Education (PGCE) afterwards. The third option is School-Centred Initial Teacher Training (SCITT) which is a graduate training programme and you do your teacher trainer year in school to gain your PGCE or QTS.

Which route do you think is best, or does that depend on the individual?

If you are fully committed to becoming a PE teacher then the way I did it was brilliant. Because I got so much teaching experience spread out over the four years. I started teaching small groups of primary school children, then progressed to full groups and on to middle and secondary schools. My last year of teaching experience was over a full term and that experience was literally like being a teacher as you are accepted as a member of staff. I think that's a really good grounding in teaching.

The flipside to studying a PE degree is you don't have the deep subject knowledge that sports science graduates have. This is because PE degrees are education-based rather than science-based so the focus is on learning how to teach. This can limit the career opportunities you have. If you are certain that you want to be a PE teacher then the route I chose is the best route but probably not if you want to keep your career options open.

Describe a typical working day as a PE teacher.

It starts with form in the morning and doing the register, and then picking things up from the day before, such as behaviour slips or dealing with emails you've had from parents. I have a pastoral role which is being the school link for the pupils and being the person in school that they can go to if they've got a problem. It also means that I have to deal with pupils when they are in trouble or have behavioural issues at school.

My timetable consists of 50% teaching practical and 50% teaching theory. The practical might be indoors or outdoors and involves teaching a range a sports and developing pupils' physical skills. The theory side involves teaching the GSCE and A-level PE syllabus which covers anatomy and physiology, sport psychology, sports history and sociology. After school I am involved in clubs as the school has sports fixtures on Tuesday and Thursday. On Wednesday after school we have a staff meeting and on Friday we meet with staff support. Monday is the only day I am free after school, so that's a day when I can catch up on some work.

I'm always surprised how much paperwork is involved in teaching. You need to be aware that PE teaching is not just about taking the football team to another school on a Tuesday night and actually there's an awful lot of paperwork and administration involved.

What advice would you give to students who wanted a career in PE teaching?

I'd say go out and get as much experience as you can. I think the best thing that you can do is get involved in sports leadership when you're young by doing courses and finding opportunities to lead sports activities. Get involved in coaching and develop the skills you need to work in a sporting environment with young people. When I did my degree at University of Bedfordshire there were 125 places and I got in through clearing, but now it's a lot more competitive as they only take about 30 students a year. Whether you get a place or not comes down to what you've done in the past and whether you've shown a willingness and a determination to go out and get practical experience. Getting experience also helps you to make sure that teaching is something you want to do and that you have a passion for it.

Also, when you have the chance get as many coaching awards as you can, such as leadership awards, as they give you good experience and make you more employable. I got awards in football, cricket and trampolining.

Which parts of your job do you enjoy the most and which parts do you enjoy less?

The reason I wanted to do the job is that I really love sport and I wanted to work in sport. But if I think about what I enjoy most about my job, it's definitely the interaction with the pupils and that relationship you build. There are highlights, such as when they are successful, and seeing them on results days or at their prom. It's really good to see children coming in in year seven and then leaving in year 11 as different people. On a day-to-day basis the thing with young people is that they are always up for a laugh and want to have a bit of fun and you can do that in PE classes. As long as you're in a positive mood and want to be energetic then the pupils will come along with you. Young people tend to be vibrant and full of life and I think being around people like that is really good for you. If you have a great lesson and everyone's been really engaged then that still gives me a real buzz.

The worst part of the job for me is dealing with Ofsted and the work around accountability. I often spend my time doing things that I don't feel adds any value to anyone. I often think that it's not helping me, it's not helping the pupils I teach, and it's just a process about inspection and accountability. It's about having things in place for inspection and that to me is a real downside.

Can you describe some of the personal skills that you need to be a PE teacher?

I think you've got to have a sense of humour to survive! The first thing a teacher needs is that you've got to be able to manage and control children. If you can't deal with and manage the children then it's not going to be possible to teach them anything. You can't do anything until you've got control and the attention of the kids. You need a bit of presence and confidence to be able to stand in front of a class and believe that these young people are going to do what you say. If they don't do what you say, then you need to be resilient to deal with that.

You need to know that some pupils can be really challenging and difficult, and you need to be patient. You have to learn to take a deep breath, be patient and calmly deal with a situation. When you lose patience and get a bit short with people that's when things don't go well, and you don't have a good day. Losing your temper is never a good thing for anyone. Showing calm authority is the thing. Also, you've got to be a bit of a performer as you've got to come into school and get yourself up for it and then go into the classroom and put on a performance bringing some energy into the room. A teacher can never have an off day or a day when they can take things a bit easier.

What opportunities for career development do you have?

The traditional career route is that you work your way up to the management of the school, from head of department then assistant head teacher, deputy head teacher and finally head teacher. However, I like the position I'm in now as I've got some autonomy over what I do, and I have a say in how the PE department is run. I'm not really involved in the leadership and management of the school, which I'm really not interested in doing. I have started doing some work with an examining board and I really enjoy that. I started off as an examiner marking exam papers and then I progressed to a team leader where you become responsible for examiners and ensuring they are marking correctly. Now I am a lead examiner where I set the exam paper and write the marks scheme. I then brief the examiners about how to mark the exam paper and monitor their progress through the marking period. I love that work and there are opportunities for progression there and the chance to stretch myself and learn new skills.

Interview 10

Richard Horner

F.A. Coach

Name

Richard Horner

Job title

Football Association (F.A.) Youth Coach Developer

Qualifications

BTEC National Diploma Sports Science

BSc (Hons) Human Movement Science, University of Liverpool

PGCE (Post-compulsory Education, University of Hertfordshire

MSc Coaching Science, Roehampton University

UEFA Pro and A Licences

Introduction

Richard is a UEFA pro qualified football coach who works for the Football Association. He is responsible for the skills development of coaches at four Premier League clubs.

What does your job entail?

My job is to help coaches become better coaches by gaining the qualifications they need and develop skills they need to perform as well as they can on a daily basis.

The rules of the Premier League dictate some of the training that coaches must undertake to work in football, such as you must be qualified to a specific standard to match the level you are coaching at. Some of the coaches I work with have already gained that required level of qualification, so they now need continual professional development (CPD), or they need to work on their development plan. In theory if everyone has the same qualification we all end up coaching in the same way, so we need to teach coaches how to do things differently. We help coaches with their personal development, which is whatever training they need to enable them to help young players they coach to become better players.

I am responsible for coach development at four London Premier League clubs and part of the F.A. team of 35 coach developers. We are the only nation who offer coaches aftercare post-qualification as opposed to just giving them the qualification and leaving them to it. You could compare it to education; where usually you study for your course and then you don't speak to your tutors after you leave and go out into the world all by yourself. We help coaches when they go out to work in their new environments.

Where are you based?

I am classed as home-based, but my diary is dictated by the clubs I work with and the demands of the national team. I'll spend two days a month at St. George's Park delivering national courses but 65% of our time needs to be spent working with the clubs that we support.

How did you get into that position?

In 1998, I started as a lecturer in sports science at West Herts College where we formed a partnership with Watford Football Club to provide education to their academy players. At the time, I was qualified as a football coach and I had people at Watford asking me if I wanted to come to the club as a coach. I had the dilemma as to whether I wanted to keep teaching sports science or become a full-time coach and help Watford's young players. I did decide to go to Watford, and I spent a few years there as a football coach and as a fitness coach for the academy players. Then I went to Chelsea as a conditioning coach where I was a coach first and foremost but they also wanted someone who can apply principles of sports science to help the academy players.

In 2006, I joined the F.A. and have had four different development roles at the F.A. Two roles within what we class as 'the whole game', which is the non-professional game at grass roots and county level. Then two roles in the professional game supporting coaches in Premier League academies and first team coaches.

What qualifications have you got?

I did a BTEC National Diploma in Sports Science whilst I was a trainee at a football club. Then I did a BSc (Hons) in Human Movement Science at University of Liverpool. After that I topped up my degree with a PGCE while I was in my first year of teaching. Then I did a Master's degree in Coaching Science at Roehampton University.

My early education was in the physical side of sport learning the principles of human movement. But my master's enabled me to apply my sports science knowledge to coaching. I am currently doing a Post-Graduate Diploma in Coaching at Leeds Beckett University with other F.A. coaches as a collective group. Although I don't particularly need another master's it is useful as it contextualises our work as coaches. At the F.A. we have partnerships with Leeds Beckett and Birmingham Universities, and they analyse our work as coaches, generate feedback from our coaching environment and start to challenge us about the processes we employ with the aim of making us better coaches.

On the football side, I have my UEFA A Licence and UEFA Pro Licence which all managers need to work in professional football. I am also a UEFA A licence and Pro Licence tutor so in terms of helping coaches I am as high as you can get as a tutor for the F.A.

What are the skills needed to be an effective coach?

I think that the answer you get depends on who you ask. I think the number one factor in the success of a coach is being able to build relationships. If you can't build relationships and you don't have good people skills you'll never get the chance to get to the point where you can work with the parts of an athlete's performance that you need to. Without having a good relationship, it is very difficult to get to the point where you can have the discussions you need to have with people.

It is difficult to assess what is meant by coaching effectiveness. Currently (in 2017) the F.A. are being judged positively as an organisation because we have had an outstanding summer with England U-20s and U-17s both winning FIFA World Cups. There are many reasons for this success, and it is the outcome of projects that we started 10 to 12 years ago. For example, we have developed better relationship with coaches in professional clubs and we are supporting their coaches at all levels. Due to these relationships, the clubs are releasing their best young players to play in international tournaments, whereas previously they may not have released the best players available for selection. Because we have the best players available then you have a better chance of success. Due to our relationships with clubs we are doing well and looking successful.

What advice would have for a person doing a BTEC qualification or a degree in sport – what would they need to do to have a successful career in coaching?

Whatever avenue you decide to take just be the best that you can be. The reason I say this is that for every football academy job in coaching there are a minimum of 150 applicants. This is because people want to work in a full time, professional coaching environment. Coaching at a football academy seems like an environment where the grass is very green. The Premier League are increasingly professionalising coaching as it has never been seen as a profession before. To achieve this there has been an increase in funding for coaching and clubs want to get the best coaches.

How can you make yourself stand out?

There will be lots of applicants with BTECs or degrees in sports science and there are also lots who have MSc and PhD qualifications. This does not necessarily mean that they are better or worse coaches but just that they may hold a higher level of qualification or competency and they may get priority in the interview process. So, what can you do to offer them something different and how can you present the best version of yourself? Do you have specific skills or specific experiences that would benefit the club? Remember that you won't even get an interview unless you have a well-presented CV or application form – you need to put serious thought into your application.

How do you balance your knowledge of theory with the reality of practice?

There are lots of coaches who have great knowledge of theory who can't apply it to help players. We also have many practitioners who don't know much about players and how to work for them. When you study a course, you learn mainly the syllabus, but the content is not always tailored towards you as a student. We teach coaches how to tailor their coaching to the players' needs rather than fit their knowledge to the players.

As an educator of coaches, I have to change my teaching every single day to meet the needs of the coaches I am training. So, make sure you are adaptable and able to change to meet the needs of players you coach. This can only be done if you have a relationship with the players you are coaching and you must get to know the players, where they are on their development journey and how they need to develop in the future. Then you can be an effective coach to those players.

As a coach, it is important to be consistent in your approach and honest in your dealings with players. If you are inconsistent players will pick up on it and a coach always needs to be fair and avoid forms of favouritism. If you show favouritism to certain players, other players will pick up on it and it will compromise your relationship with a group of players.

If we are consistent, honest, fair and our behaviours remain true we tend to get better at everything we do.

Useful resources

Football Association coaching courses

http://www.facoachingcourses.org.uk/uefa-a-licence.html

BTEC Nationals in Sport and Exercise Science

http://qualifications.pearson.com/en/qualifications/btec-nationals/sport-and-exercise-science-2016.html

Interview 11

Anthony Limbrick

Football Manager/Head Coach

Name

Anthony Limbrick

Job title

Manager – Woking F.C.

Qualifications

UEFA Pro Licence 2017/18 Cohort - English FA
UEFA A Licence / Diploma - English FA
UEFA B Licence / FA Level 3 Certificate in Coaching Football
FA Level 2 Certificate in Coaching Football

FA Youth Award Module 4 - 'Advanced Youth Award'
FA Youth Award Module 3 – 'Developing the Player'
FA Youth Award Module 2 – 'Developing the Practice'
FA Youth Award Module 1 – 'Developing the Environment'

Introduction

Anthony Limbrick was manager at non-league Woking F.C. during the 2017-2018 season and in summer 2018 he became assistant manager at Grimsby Town F.C. Originally from Australia, he came to England to become a professional footballer but at a young age he sustained a serious injury. He wanted to stay in football so decided he was going to become a coach but found himself without any coaching qualifications or coaching experience. Anthony has worked in a range of coaching roles, including working with future England internationals and managing a National League club.

How has your career developed?

My coaching career has been very different to most people's as I don't know anyone who has had such a vast array of coaching jobs. I'm not sure I'd necessarily recommend it as some of things that I have been through have been difficult.

People often think that to become a coach you'll go to university and get a degree and some coaching qualifications and then fall into a football academy job and start working with some of the best players in the country. But for me it just didn't work like that.

I started playing football in Australia, but I always knew I wanted to move to the UK. In Australia we always followed English football and my family would stay up and watch matches, such as the F.A. Cup final, and follow the major tournaments. I thought I was a good player when I was 18 or 19 but when I got to England I started to realise how difficult it was and how tough it was playing in the lower leagues. I travelled around England, Wales and Scotland and couldn't find a club that would have me. I ended up playing semi-professional football but then I broke my leg.

I did recover and played again but decided to retire from full-time football and become a coach with the aim of coaching at the top level. I'm not fully sure why but I think it was because I had always been a student of the game without realising it. I would study each position on the pitch, what each player did, and the demands placed on them. I also studied nutrition, psychology and other aspects of sports science. I realised I had knowledge that I could put into practice through a coaching career.

My first job was at a company called Active Planet, who ran after schools' sports clubs in primary schools. This involved teaching multi-sports and it was my first experience of coaching. I had no real idea about what I was doing, and often thought 'how can I make the leap to coaching top football players from working with young children here?' But I went in with the mentality that every session was a challenge for me to motivate these young people. When you are working with four- or five-year olds you still have to motivate them before you can teach them anything. That is no different to the work I do now with first team players or the work I did at Southampton working with England internationals. I learnt very early on to make every session the best session whatever the challenges.

If you want to get into coaching any sport you've got to do as much coaching as you can to develop experience. Some people will coach for four hours a week and then observe other coaches for 10 hours and think they are improving. You can watch other coaches all you want but you've got to go and deliver yourself. I've coached at many different levels and have done so many hours taking the same session a hundred times over to change it and make it better. It may sound obvious, but you've got to keep delivering to get better. If you are a piano player, you don't spend all your time watching other piano players - you practice yourself. Watching other coaches is important in learning but maybe the ratio should be 10% watching and 90% doing. Many coaches think you've got to watch the best coaches to become better but, in my opinion, you've got to do it yourself.

After working for Active Planet where did you go next?

From there I went to Borehamwood Football Club in North London to work with players on their college scheme. During the day I would coach players who hadn't made it in the professional game and had gone back to college to complete their education. By this point I had got my F.A. Levels 1 and 2 coaching qualifications. I was very fortunate that when I did my coaching courses I learnt a lot from them as I did them at the right time in my career. Some people go on the courses just to collect their badges and often think they know more than they are being taught. I didn't really know much so I learnt a lot on the Level 2 course due to the stage my career was at.

At Borehamwood I coached older age groups for the first time so learnt a lot from that. I was playing semi-professional for Wingate and Finchley and became the first team coach and then assistant manager there. I was only about 23 at the time and I could hardly fit the time in - I was coaching at Borehamwood during the day and then working with senior men at Wingate and Finchley in the evenings. I would easily coach over 10 sessions a week as well as playing two or three times. It was hectic, and because I'd never coached senior men before I had to adapt to coaching these men some of whom were 10 years older than me and had played a lot more football than I had. I had to somehow get them to buy into what I was trying to do. I had some terrible coaching moments there thinking 'what am I doing here?' But it taught me that if you can motivate a plumber who has been at work since 5 am then it is easy to coach professional footballers because they are solely focused on learning and improving their football.

After leaving Borehamwood I got a job with the Football Association (F.A.) working on their Skills Programme. It was interesting because at Borehamwood I had moved away from coaching junior football and was now going back. I decided to take the job because it was with the F.A. and I knew I would be able to do my UEFA A licence coaching qualification and find out about learning and development. While I knew a lot about football I didn't know how to apply that knowledge to players or the best methods of coaching. Going to work for the F.A. and discovering about coaching and pedagogy and learning from other people was the best kind of education I could get. Particularly finding out about how children learn and develop, and how to use differentiation in sessions was so valuable.

I gained my UEFA A license at this time as I felt that to gain credibility as a young coach who had never played professional football I needed to get qualified early. I was 27 when I passed which is quite young. I knew that was the stepping stone I needed to work in Academy football. I didn't see how working in non-league football would take me where I wanted to go quickly enough, and I had always wanted to work in academies and work with the best players I could. Now I was qualified and was doing well on the Skills Programme the opportunity came up to work at the Southampton Academy as full-time under-14 coach.

At this point Southampton were employing full-time coaches in their academies even though they were in League One at the time. I was fortunate to see Southampton progress to the Premiership during the four years that I coached there. I had also completed F.A. youth modules 1 and 2 that sit alongside the A and B licences and along with my A licence and coaching experience I got the job at Southampton. I never thought I was going to get the job as my CV showed I lacked any experience coaching at an academy. The interview process was made up of two parts with an interview followed by a coaching session and I was confident because I had so much coaching experience.

During the interview I was grilled by the director of football about my lack of experience and how I had never worked with top players so when it came to the coaching session I just thought I'm not going to get this job, but it will be a good experience to work with these top players for a day. But I got the job and talking to the director of football afterwards he said that when he saw me coach he thought 'we can work with him because he can deliver coaching'. Getting jobs is not always about using your contacts as at some point you've got to be able to deliver what is needed or else you are going to get found out.

It seems to me that you have made the most of your training opportunities which is something that not everyone does.

I think a lot of people do courses to get the badge and then use it to try and get a job. Maybe I was fortunate that when I did coaching courses I didn't know much about that level of coaching. For example, when I did the UEFA B licence I didn't know how to structure sessions. Now I am doing the UEFA Pro licence I am gaining so much knowledge that I can use in my management. I still go back through to the text books and pick things up. As a coach you need to keep going back and look at the basics to keep your knowledge topped up.

I would add in that that I have been turned down for so many jobs. I couldn't even tell you the number of jobs that I have applied for and been laughed at or not even been close to getting. I have had so many setbacks, particularly when I was out of work. You will always get setbacks, or there will be jobs you should have got that are given to someone else, and you must be able to deal with them and push through the disappointment.

How long did you work at Southampton for?

I was there for four years, which was two years with the U14s, one year with the U16s and one with the U18s. During that time, I was fortunate to be able to also work with the U21s during the day as the younger age groups trained in the evenings. I worked with future England internationals, such as Luke Shaw, James Ward-Prowse and Calum Chambers who were in the U18s. I got a broad range of experience by coaching across all age groups and I think this really helped me develop as a coach. When you become a higher profile coach you also get involved in things like talking to the media and I had to pretend to know what I was doing when I really didn't.

I have also been lucky to have had senior managers as mentors. Nigel Adkins has offered me tips and advice now I am a manager myself. It was also great to watch Mauricio Pochettino working with young players as he is one of the best coaches I have seen. I still watch a lot of football, more to analyse play than for pleasure. I'll record a Sunday match and watch it throughout the week and maybe analyse how midfielders break forwards and then apply it to my own coaching.

After working at Southampton, I went back to Australia for a while to deal with some family issues and take a break because life had been hectic. I came back to England and got a job at West Ham Football Academy where I worked with the U15 and U16 teams.

It was another good club to have on my CV and I worked with some good people. It gave me the chance to spend more time on the grass coaching and I wouldn't do a job if I couldn't spend time coaching. In modern football the managers are really coaches now as they have directors of football to do all the transfers and business side. Managers spend time working with and developing players to make them better so are probably head coaches. My style of management is to coach every day and take every session I can.

When you were manager at Woking what would you do on a typical day?

I would get up at 5 am and travel to the Woking training ground to be there for 7 am It's an early start but I needed to start the day with a planning meeting for the staff. We'd already prepared the training session the day before and we'd meet so that everyone would know what they were doing. We would discuss what was happening with the injured players and what each player would be doing in the session. The players came in at 10 am but we would have set up by 9.30 am so everything was ready when the players arrived. We wanted to be professional and so everything was ready for the players. When the players came in I'd always have a chat with them or meet with three or four players if there were things I wanted to go through with them or show them some video to give them feedback. At 10.30 am we would have a meeting with the players and maybe go through some video footage or we would start training then. The sessions generally ran from 10.30 am until midday and we'd then have lunch. Sometimes we would do another session from 2 pm to 3 pm but that often just with individuals; for example, taking the full backs to do some work on their crossing.

After training I'd go back to my office and maybe have another meeting, speak to the board of the football club and get my plans sorted out for the next day. I'd make sure I saw everyone at the club, so I'd go and see the secretary, talk to the people who do the cleaning and see everyone involved at the club. It's so important to speak to everyone in the club no matter how big or small their role is at the club. Then I'd prepare my plans for the next day. I'd also spend a lot of time on the phone. I never realised, until I became a manager, that everyone wants to talk to you – agents want to talk about their players, players want to call you. No-one ever wanted to speak to me before and now I am a manager everyone does.

By the time I got home it could be as late as 10 pm. Also, there may have a midweek fixture and I wouldn't get home until 3 am and then have to be back in work for a meeting the next day at 9 am. The hours are long if you do the job properly. You could get away with finishing at 1 pm but I've never been able to do that. Even when I worked at academies the hours were long because I'd get in at 8 am, work with the academy players during the day and then coach younger age groups in the evening until after 8 pm.

As a coach the hours are long, and that impacts on social life and family life, so it is a big commitment. It also takes a special person, my wife, to support that commitment. Especially in the early years when the hours are long and pay is poor. Not many people can hold out until things improve, especially if they have a family. If you work at a professional club the pay is better, but the job is less secure as you could be fired at any time or your club could be relegated. I had little choice as I dropped out of high school and had few formal qualifications apart from my coaching awards, so I had to make it work otherwise I would have had nothing. A smart person would study and get a degree, so they have something to fall back on if their coaching career didn't work out.

What advice would you have for people who want a career in coaching?

Just spend as much time as you can coaching. I've worked in so many different types of environments – coaching three and four-year olds, multi-sports coaching, in a classroom, working with troubled teenagers, men's football, women's football. All those sessions helped me to be more adaptable as a coach. For example, at Southampton I might be half way through a session and the manager tells me they are taking five or six players from my session. I must adapt the session to make up for the loss of players and I think I could do that due to the different experiences I had had before. Even if you are coaching seven-year-old players you can use what you learn and apply it to coaching adults or professionals.

Are there other opportunities for sports science graduates to work at Woking FC or other clubs?

We had a programme where we took a sports science student from Southampton Solent University on a placement to do video analysis and other work for us. As a small club in the National League we didn't have enough money to employ full time sports scientists but could offer placements and internships. After this there may be an opportunity to carry on working with us in some capacity. This also happened at Southampton and West Ham where we took students on a placement year and found excellent coaches and sports scientists in this way. We had to take students in their placement year and worked together with the University to set goals for their time with us.

Interview 12

Matt Kleinman

Football Agent

Name

Matt Kleinman

Job title

Football agent

Qualifications

BA (Hons) Leisure Studies, University of Birmingham

BTEC National Diploma in Leisure Studies, West Herts College

Introduction

Matt is a football agent who represents professional footballers at all levels of the professional games. He is involved in negotiating with clubs to get the best contracts for his players and also in organising and planning many aspects of the lives of players that he represents.

What qualifications have you got for the role that you're in?

I went to West Herts College in Watford to do a BTEC National in Leisure Studies in 1993 and that got me on to a BA (Hons) Leisure Studies degree at Birmingham University. However, I've got to say that none of my education has much relevance to my current role in the football industry, as it's about who you know and not what you know. I fell into this business because I used to play football.

How did that work?

I got my job because I used to play football at a semi-professional level with a South African who happened to be a lawyer by profession. He had his own small practice where he was practicing immigration law but was also a football agent representing leading South African players that were playing in Europe at the time. That was players like Lucas Radebe at Leeds United, Mark Fish at Bolton and Shaun Bartlett who played for Charlton Athletic. There were a lot of South African players who came to England in the mid to late 90s and he asked me if I wanted to go and do some work experience with him.

I was actually looking at going into sports sponsorship and wanted to get some work experience. I had approached Nike and tailored my dissertation towards trying to get a job with them. I struggled to get any feedback from them on my dissertation so that ended up as a failed attempt and a false start. I jumped at the chance to go and work with this South African lawyer and after a short probationary period he employed me on a very modest wage. My role there grew from writing articles on these players for South Africa football magazines to looking after their insurance policies and doing anything for them off the pitch that they needed sorting out.

So I became very friendly with them and their families and eventually the South African lawyer emigrated to the US to get married and I inherited some of his players. I soon moved onto another agency run by sports lawyer, Mel Stein. Mel is well-known for having represented Paul Gascoigne, Alan Shearer, Neil Lennon and numerous other top talents.

At this stage I had no formal qualification to be a football agent. To be an agent you needed to pass an exam set by the English F.A. You had to pay £500 to take the exam and if you passed you had to pay an indemnity insurance to cover yourself and then you could represent footballers.

It was a multiple-choice exam about regulations pertaining to FIFA and the F.A. about the transfers of players domestically and internationally, how to resolve disputes and all sorts of legal matters. It wasn't simple and straight forward and you had to achieve a certain pass mark to get your licence. I passed it the second time I took it. Up until that time in the early 2000s I wasn't officially representing footballers or negotiating their contracts. Other people were negotiating the contracts and doing the financial terms and signing off on the deals. I was managing and looking after the players' needs on a daily basis.

Since then the industry has changed and become totally deregulated. Now you need absolutely no qualifications to become an agent. So anyone can become a football agent today if they wanted to. You pay £500, fill out a form, get a DBS check done and you're good to go. So you can understand now how players' brothers, cousins, parents, friends, or anyone can claim to be an agent. Players are being pulled in all directions and then being poorly represented. There is so much money in football and players are being managed by unregulated agents and that's why it's become an unscrupulous profession.

At what level do footballers start having an agent?

Legally I can only represent a player when they're aged 16, or in the year of their 16th birthday. When you sign a representation contract with a 16-year old player the parent has to sign it off as well or their legal guardian has to be party to that contract up until the age of 18. An agent's contract with a player at any age can only last a maximum of two years at any one time. A contract can be torn up and they can re-sign for another agent for a two-year period at any time, but the contract cannot be for longer than two years for any one period.

What does your job entail on a daily basis?

I think the beauty of what I do is that no one day is the same as the next. Our business is very different from other businesses in that there are only really two windows of opportunity where you can make any money. Those are the two transfer windows - the summer window which lasts for about three months and the January window which lasts for one month. You can understand why there may be some unscrupulous activity because people only have a very short period in which to make any money. But the amount they make can be great. During these periods everyone's jostling for position. Some people are working on behalf of the clubs, some people are working on behalf of players and some people are trying to muscle in on other agent's players.

My job in January or July is very different to February when the transfer window's closed. Outside of transfer windows my job involves speaking to players who aren't our clients right now, finding out who they're with, how long they've got left on their contracts and whether they're happy with their representation. If they're contracted to someone there's not a great deal we can do about that other than stay in touch. If their situation changes then they might want to change agency, then we're in a position to help them. More importantly we're dealing with the clients that we have right now. There may be an opportunity for them to move on to a better situation or to move somewhere else because they're not playing regularly at their current club. That might be a loan move or a permanent transfer to a better opportunity for them. This is on top of working with them on a daily basis.

We really look after most of their needs and this could be sourcing a new car for them, helping them get a mortgage on a property or putting their dogs in kennels because their wife is going on holiday. I've done all sorts of things. I've stayed at a client's house because his wife has panic attacks if she's there by herself. As I say, no one day is the same as the next. Often I'm out watching games, going to meetings, finding out which players are available or talking to our players to see if they've got friends who aren't happy with their agents and if we can help at all. I collaborate with agents abroad to see whether they've got players they want to bring over and play here, and if we can help and speak to clubs about their needs and requirements.

What personal skills do you think you need to be a successful football agent?

I like to think my strengths are in dealing with people. But my strengths happen to also be my weaknesses in this kind of industry in that I'm an honest person and that doesn't necessarily fit well within this industry unfortunately.

There's no doubt you need a lot of perseverance. You need to be somebody who doesn't take rejection personally because you're going to face a lot of that from players who either don't answer the phone or promise you something and then let you down. There's a lack of loyalty in this industry. So if you take rejection badly and personally then you're not going to stay in it for a long time.

Because there are so many agents out there it's hard to break into the profession in the first place. But if you have a passion for something and you believe you're going to be good at it you should pursue it until all avenues have been explored. Until you've exhausted all opportunities and you can look yourself in the mirror and say, 'I know I've given it everything I've got'. I think one of my strengths is if I'm being told I can't do something I use that as a personal driver to make sure that I prove that person wrong. I make it my personal mission to help my clients get where they want to be.

I like to think I have lots of perseverance and self-belief knowing that I do my business the right way. I think a lot of people in this industry don't. I think there's a lack of intelligence and a lack of integrity. I think if you have basic skills such as a good work ethic, integrity and an ability to communicate well with people you can do well in this industry.

Is there anything else that is important?

This work is about being able to build relationships with players and with clubs and that takes time. In any intensely competitive industry you're only as strong as the contacts you've got and can maintain. Unfortunately, players can be very fickle and often all they care about is themselves. There was one player who broke my heart. He is now an England player, but I represented him from a young age, and I got on so well with him and I got on brilliantly with his family. I used to go to their house for Sunday lunch and was there to watch him play when he scored on his debut for England under-18s in his home town. I looked after him for about four years and during that time there were periods when he wasn't playing, and things weren't going so well. One of my greatest memories in this business was when he had finally started to fulfil his potential and he got called up to play for England. It was such a buzz; it was such a good feeling. But when he came towards the end of the contract, he got tapped up by someone else saying we can get you this contract and he left me and was sold to a big club in a multimillion-pound deal. You'd like to think there's a bit more loyalty from players than there is but there isn't, and while they don't normally get to me that one did. Yes, developing relationships is important but sometimes no matter how good the relationship it doesn't always count for much.

Which parts of your job do you enjoy and are there any parts that you dislike?

The parts that I dislike are that I don't like the disloyalty in the industry. I pride myself on being a loyal person and a totally transparent one who deals with people with integrity. Anything that works against that belief I don't enjoy. The thing I enjoy the most is that I love being involved in football. That was a big driver for me when I first started in this industry. What I love the most is seeing a young player grow and develop and play football for the first team or play for their country. Being there when they make their debut or score their first goal and being around them and their family is just such a buzz. It's such an amazing feeling that you can't replace. Just feeling part of that development and part of that success is incredible. You know, forget the money, which can be great, for me the real buzz is seeing a player grow, develop and fulfil their potential and being part of their success.

Additional resources

How to become a football agent

https://playerscout.co.uk/careers-in-football/football-agent/how-to-become-a-football-agent/

F.A. policy on working as an intermediary (agent)

http://www.thefa.com/football-rules-governance/policies/intermediaries/intermediaries-registration

Interview 13

Richard Marfell

Personal Trainer

Name

Richard Marfell

Job title

Wellness coach/Personal Trainer (Home training)

Qualifications

Premier Diploma in Personal Training

Introduction

Richard is a personal trainer who retrained after a first career in Design. He trains people in environments outside of the gym, such as in their houses or in parks and open spaces. He also offers sports massage and nutritional advice to his clients.

What does your job involve?

I train people in their own homes and also offer sports massage, nutrition advice and listening therapy. I work with my clients in a variety of environments, although most of the time it is in their homes, in their private gyms, and sometimes in the summer we train outside. I bring the training equipment in my car and this includes dumbbells, kettlebells, cables, a step, stability balls and an exercise mat.

Each training session lasts one hour, and I schedule thirty minutes between sessions for travel and setting up time. My main role is to instruct exercises and design exercise programmes. I used to do some fitness testing as well but now I do very little. The only thing I do is weigh people and take their body fat if they want me to. I usually get weight loss clients to measure their progress by seeing how many holes on their belt they have dropped.

How did you get into your current job?

At school, I did A-levels before doing a BA in Design at Bristol University. I went into full time employment in the exhibition industry and worked in it until I was 38. At that point, I realised the design industry was rapidly changing as people were coming in with less design knowledge than me but better IT skills. Either I needed to develop my IT skills or change career.

I went to a careers advisor who did a personality test with me. The test showed that my current job did not suit my personality very well. However, to retrain could take me three or four years and my family commitments meant that I couldn't afford this time. I had to look at shorter courses and we came up with two ideas - one was personal training and the other one was landscape design.

I went to see the landscape design training company but there was no one there to see me. So, I went to Premier training, who are a company offering personal training courses, and there I met with the careers adviser and course instructor. After a conversation with them I realised a career in personal training was a possibility for me. It was a Wednesday and there was a three-month course starting on the next Monday so I thought 'well, I'll just do it'.

Initially, I was very nervous as I was nearly 40 and I thought everyone else was going to be about 18. I tackled this by getting to the course early, meeting the trainers and the other students. As I was there first it felt like it was my environment that people were coming into so that made me comfortable. The course cost a significant amount of money so I sat at the front where there were no distractions as I wanted to be absorbed in it.

How did your career progress after your training?

Once I had qualified I kept some of my previous work and went to work in a gym as a personal trainer. I quickly realised that the training course was just a start as I actually knew nothing about working as a personal trainer. There is a lot of learning to do about how to handle situations and working in a new environment. The gym environment was ideal as I was supported and I learnt to adapt to it. I slowly did more and more personal training and less design work before going out on my own and doing home training.

What would be a typical day or week for you?

I have between 40-50 people on my client base and I can't train all of them all the time. I can do up to six clients a day and the most I have had on one day is eight clients. The problem with having eight clients is that it equates to 12-13 hours of work when you include travel in between. I can train three clients back to back before having a break so I may do three clients in the morning and then three in the late afternoon/evening. Often, I won't get home until 9-9.30 pm. I say I don't work at the weekends, but I will do an occasional session if I can't keep a client happy during the week. So, I do around 30 training sessions a week. You need to be careful not to do seven days a week or you will quickly burn out. You also need to learn to say 'no' if necessary.

I also spend a lot of time sorting out my online diary. One thing I learnt quickly was that you need to be flexible. For example, yesterday was a good example of how things can change quickly as the day before I had six clients scheduled in my diary with the first one at 8 am. I allow half an hour between clients to get from A to B and a break in the middle for lunch. However, by the evening before I was down to three clients as one client had hurt their ankle, one had an appointment more important than training and one had flu. However, this meant I could offer training sessions to clients that I had previously told that I had a full diary.

What are the pros and cons of working in home training?

When you train people in a gym the onus is on them to make the effort to get there and they can cancel without even talking to you. However, when you visit people in their homes training is much easier for them as they don't have to leave their house and all they have to do is get changed.

One issue with home training is that you don't have such a wide choice of equipment as you are limited by what you can get into your car. There is time wasted getting to the client's house and getting training equipment out of the car and set up. Once you have done the hour you have 30 minutes to get to the next client but 10 or 15 minutes can be eaten up by loading the car, making the next appointment and having a chat. So, you are not just doing an hour, you are doing an hour plus 15 minutes for a chat and about 10 minutes for setting up. Add in the time it takes to get there and it is closer to two hours, but you only get paid for the time you train them. Whereas in a gym you can train clients back to back without travel time and time spent moving equipment. The bonus with home training you get to keep 100% of the money and don't have to give a proportion to the gym or pay them rent.

Travel can be a little stressful, particularly if you get behind time and if you get stressed you may not be in the right frame of mind to train clients. Travel must be really tough in busy places like London.

There can be distractions, for example, I sometimes get children joining in if they are at home. While this can be a distraction it can make sessions fun. I have clients I train outside in a small group of five clients all of whom are mums. I have had a situation where I was training five mums and their five children. Also, cats and dogs often get involved as well and while it is challenging it is nice that everyone gets some exercise.

Group sessions can be a social catch up for the group as well as a training session. You must not be too sensitive or precious and allow them time to chat and joke with each other. Quite often when they come to pay they will give me a bit more for the hard work I've done.

What are the personal skills that are needed to be a successful trainer?

Success is all about personality and the skills needed vary depending on your training environment, client base and your location. Above all you need to be able to empathise, listen and interact with people. You need to be able to talk to people about things like politics, sport, cats, dogs, anything. I have learnt a lot from the people I train and hopefully they have learnt a lot from me. You then build up a relationship and you can exchange things. For example, I have had people help me with business ideas, mortgages and health issues. You also get acts of kindness with people giving you vegetables from their garden or free tickets for sporting events.

You need to be very adaptable and flexible. I make sure that I tailor exercise to the client's needs on the day. In the early days of my personal training career I would prepare programmes before visiting my clients, then go along with a variety of equipment and instruct the session. Now I have a conversation with the client as we warm up so I can gauge how the client feels and whether they have any injuries or other problems. Then I'll adjust training to suit them.

Training has got to be about what the client wants, not what I want. I have tried pushing people to do more than they want to do but it ends up being a less enjoyable session for them. They need to get some enjoyment from the session or it ends up being something they won't look forward to or continue.

Listening to your client, observing them and getting a feeling for how they are reacting are the most important things.

It seems that developing the relationship is important.

I think so as I have seen trainers who can be very robotic in their approach. They don't adapt to their clients' needs and are not flexible. I've seen people training where no one says anything, apart from the trainer saying 'give me another five reps'. Unless they are very good trainers and get great results that relationship is not going to last very long. Equally if you are training and you don't get on with your client you must ask yourself whether it is beneficial to continue that relationship. You may think they will get on better with someone else and you've got to do what's right for your client.

What advice would you have for people who want to follow a similar career path to yours?

You should talk to people in the industry who are working in gyms or doing personal training and find out about the reality of working in the fitness industry. It's good to have a niche to fit into, such as training sports people or people with specific medical conditions; so talk to trainers who are doing different things. There are a lot of trainers out there so find what you enjoy and don't worry about what other trainers are doing. People will be attracted to you because of your personality and what you offer.

Also think about appearance as that goes with being professional. It is important to look good and have appropriate clothing. I have my logo on my training gear and some people put branding stickers on their cars but I don't. You also need to look after your fitness equipment and keep it clean. It shows that you care and how can you look after other people if you can't look after yourself. Also, be honest with your clients and be 'human'. For example, saying that you eat junk food occasionally allows them to relate to you better. Being completely obsessed with your own body and having perfect nutritional habits can provide an unobtainable standard for your clients to live up to.

Are there any parts of the job you find less enjoyable?

I don't enjoy getting stuff in and out of the car, particularly on a wet day. Everything can get muddy and then you've got to put the equipment in your car or onto someone's cream carpet. Always having equipment in my car annoys me and it can look like I am living in my car. I've injured my elbow just getting stuff in and out of the car. The limited variety of training kit is an issue as you can't use cable machines, heavy weights or treadmills that you would have in a gym. Also, warming up people can be difficult with just a step to use.

What are the best things about your job?

There are many things I love about my career. I have the chance to meet many lovely, interesting and sometimes inspiring people. I get to visit some amazing houses and train in a variety of outside venues, from barns to playing fields whilst encountering all sorts of weather. Training outside in the summer and winter can be challenging but always exciting, especially as the seasons change. Beats a desk job anyway! I have been paid to walk, trek, run, jog and cycle with my clients.

I enjoy exchanging views on topics other than fitness and health and this helps breaks down barriers and allows for a fun time during sessions. I am very lucky to be able to help and support as well as impart knowledge to my clients. All this makes my life worthwhile. I get particular satisfaction when I see a positive change in a client's attitude, changes in their shape and loss of weight, clients developing new habits or increasing their happiness levels – these things make me happy too. The results I have achieved, friends and contacts I have made and some wonderful comments I have received have improved my life for the better.

Additional resources

Richard Marfell's website

http://richardmarfell.uk/home/4590743735

Premier Training courses

https://www.premierglobal.co.uk/courses/

Interview 14

Ronique Redelinghuys

Personal Trainer and Sports Massage Therapist

Name

Ronique Redelinghuys

Job title

Sports massage therapist and personal trainer

Qualifications

BSc (Hons) Biokinetics, University of Pretoria

Vinyasa and Power Flow Yoga Teacher

Diploma in Clinical Pilates

Advanced Diploma in Pilates

Advanced Sports Massage

Introduction

Ronique is a sports massage therapist and personal trainer who is based on Necker Island, which is part of the British Virgin Islands in the Caribbean. Necker Island is Sir Richard Branson's private island that can be hired out to guests. Ronique is personal trainer to Sir Richard and his family and she also teaches Pilates and yoga to guests on the island. She also offers sports massage treatments from the spa located on the island. She is originally from South Africa.

What does your job entail?

As a personal trainer, I train Sir Richard and his family and any guests on the island who want personal training. Sir Richard likes to train in the gym as well as play tennis twice a day. The Branson family also take part in events such as Strive and the London Marathon. Strive is a mass participation event across four weeks involving cycling, running, rowing and walking that is done to raise money for the Big Change charity. It finishes with a climb up Mont Blanc. The family need to be fit enough to cope with these extreme demands.

We often have guests who have personal trainers at home, so I'll continue their work as they like to keep up with their training. Whether that is working on cardiovascular fitness, increasing muscle mass or keeping on with their Pilates and yoga.

I also run Pilates and yoga classes for guests in the mornings and work from the spa doing sports massage and rehabilitation work.

Tell me about your education

After high school in South Africa I went to study Human Movement Sciences at University of Pretoria and completed a BSc (Hons) in Biokinetics. Biokinetics is a bit like sports therapy and biokineticists work hand-in-hand with physiotherapists. The physiotherapist deals with the initial pain phase where they have just become injured and the affected part is inflamed. Then the biokineticists steps in to complete their rehabilitation phase and work on their strength and conditioning.

I then did courses in yoga, Pilates and advanced Pilates and also sports massage and normal massage therapy.

This gives me a wide variety of skills that I can use. I come at personal training from a sports conditioning perspective and start by conditioning clients' muscles to prepare them for specific sports or activities and then start to work towards their goals of hypertrophy or endurance. I always make sure they are conditioned and start by dealing with any injuries and fixing any postural imbalances before doing any heavy weights or training. Weight training on a poor posture can produce injuries and muscle imbalances that will affect them when they start their training programme.

Do you find that sports rehabilitation and personal training complement each other well?

Yes, and studying both has given me more knowledge. Personal training courses are often quite short, and you don't always get to know and understand physiology in depth. You may not always understand which muscles are agonists and which are antagonists in a movement, how these muscles are contracting, and which muscles are working around a joint. You need this knowledge to know what your training is actually doing for a person. A lot of instructor training focuses on exercises and training techniques and learning as much as you can about them and not about how to fix any problems they may have. Often clients don't really know what their goals should be, as they say they want to lose weight or build muscle but it can be more complex than that. Trainers often give clients what they say they want which is not always best for them at that point. For me, it is important to make sure that I don't cause any damage or pain to a client.

How did you get to your position today?

After I had graduated, I worked with a rugby team at a university in Pretoria and a local rugby team called the Blue Bulls. Then I went to work for a company called Techno Gym researching into people who had high risk conditions, such as high blood pressure, diabetes and other metabolic syndromes. In particular, we looked at the effect exercise had on these conditions and which types of exercise were best. After about two years I went into private practice working with two physiotherapists. They would send their clients to me after they have treated them during their initial inflammation phase. I would treat them until they had a low level of pain and I would train them to fix any postural issues. It was personal training with aspects of rehabilitation within it. People usually get an injury due to a predisposition or a postural problem, such as kyphosis, that limits range of motion at their shoulder. I would fix that problem, so it doesn't reoccur when they return to their sport or training. Then in 2018 I moved to Necker Island to work as a personal trainer.

In September 2017 there was a massive hurricane that destroyed large parts of the British Virgin Islands including Necker Island. My partner, Mike, had previously been working on Necker as a kiteboarding instructor and he was rehired in June 2018 when the island was habitable again. I searched the Virgin Limited Edition careers website for jobs and they were advertising a role as a personal trainer and yoga teacher with additional skills instructing water sports. I applied for the role and was interviewed via Skype. I was offered the job as I had all the skills that they required.

What personal skills do you think you need in your working role?

I think you need to be confident, be able to listen, be patient and teach your client patience so they can achieve their long-term goals. You need to be able to communicate and talk to your client so that you can find out what they want and also get to know what they are capable of physically, their strengths and weaknesses, and any physical problems they have with their body.

How did you get the skills of confidence, communication and patience?

Partly from doing so many courses. I know such a range of exercise and techniques and I can draw on them within a second. As soon as I see that someone is struggling with an exercise, I can change it to something else, or if it is boring or not challenging, I can make it harder. I have many different exercises from my personal training, yoga and Pilates courses that I can draw from.

I am an introvert, so I much prefer working one-to-one than with a large group. I have had to teach myself to talk to larger groups of people and that comes with practice. I try to chat to as many people as possible in the class and ask them questions so I can talk less. Also asking them questions is a good way to get to know them better and then feel more comfortable with them. People don't always think I am an introvert but it's not a bad thing as I am good at listening to people and remembering things about them. If you do find it difficult to talk to people then asking them questions and making them talk it makes it easier for you. It's also good for them as most people like to talk and you find out more about them.

What do you like about your job and are there any parts of your job that you don't like so much?

I like helping people achieve their goals and seeing what they can achieve. I like motivating people – it's great when you can motivate someone to achieve their goals. Also motivating people to move away from something; for example if someone is experiencing stress, you can get their mind to move away from what is worrying them to thinking about themselves.

I find it difficult when people aren't patient and want their goals quickly, in the week or so when they are on the island. I always tell people that if they don't train at least three times a week then they won't change their body and reach their goals. It does take about 10 weeks of training to see real change. You may feel different in two to three weeks, but physical changes do take longer. People forget it has taken them about 10 years to get into their current state and I am not a miracle worker who can fix a body in two weeks.

What advice would you give someone who wanted a career like yours?

I would say that you really need to have a good knowledge of anatomy and physiology. You really need to understand how the body works and in particular how muscles work, what muscles do, where they attach and how they work as agonists and antagonists. You need enough knowledge so that you don't cause any injuries. You will change someone's body if they train with you for months and if you just train one muscle of an antagonist pair then you will set up serious imbalances in the body leading to poor posture and injury.

Also mix up what you are learning. There are so many courses that you can study online to further your education. The more skills you have the better and things like spinning, yoga and Pilates are really useful to have. Pilates and yoga are great to have if you have just studied sports science as they can help with rehabilitation and are great for learning about stretching and core strength. You can look at yoga as being a fitness modality if you want, but some people see it as a spiritual modality.

Finally, don't stick to one type of exercise – the more skills you have then the more clients you can work with, more types of injuries you can work with. You won't get bored and your clients won't get bored and there will be no situation that you won't be able to deal with.

Where do you see your career progressing in the future?

I would love to have my own personal training studio with sports massage, yoga and Pilates in South Africa. Working on an island is a good way to save money so in around three years I would like to be able to open my own place and then employ other people to work with me.

Additional resource

Virgin Limited Edition careers

https://www.virginlimitededition.com/en/careers#current-opportunities

Interview 15

Lisa Kelly

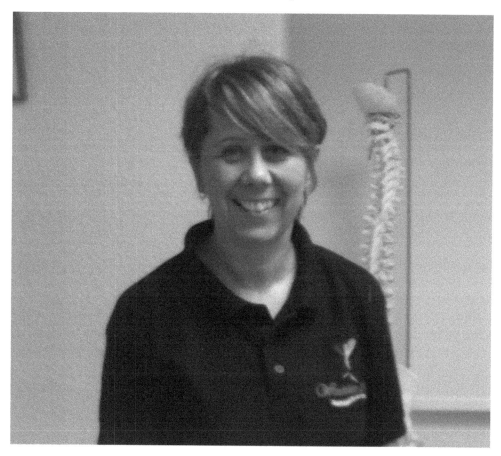

Sports Massage Therapist

Name

 Lisa Kelly

Job title

Sports massage therapist/soft tissue therapist

Qualifications

Diploma in Sports Massage

Advanced Diploma in Sports Massage and Rehabilitation

Introduction

Lisa is a self-employed sports massage therapist who treats a range of clients that are suffering from musculoskeletal problems. She combines her rehabilitation work with teaching and examining.

What is your job title?

I am a sports massage therapist regulated by the Sports Massage Association (SMA) and we also call ourselves soft tissue therapists. The SMA found that calling what we do sports massage was possibly giving out the wrong impression to people that you had to be involved in sport in order to have a sports massage. Obviously that's not the case as many of my clients experience occupational and postural stresses and pain rather than sports related injuries. Now we refer to soft tissue as it encompasses the issues experienced by many people rather than just those that are involved in sport. So I am a sports massage therapist, but we also call ourselves soft tissue therapists.

Where and how do you work?

I work in two ways and am self-employed. I am based at a clinic called Woodside and they've got practices in Leighton Buzzard and Dunstable. Although I work privately and am self-employed I come under their umbrella but am not employed by them. I also work on a self-employed basis from a place in Buckingham called Taylor Made. It's predominantly a beauty therapy practice, but there is also a physiotherapist, chiropractor and me. I have to promote my own business and I rent a room from them. At the Woodside clinic they give me the clients and we work on a 50/50 basis there. So even though I'm self-employed I take 50% and they take 50% of the income.

What does your job entail on a daily basis?

When a client comes to me, I start with a full medical assessment. I have to make sure that all the notes that I take are accurate, comprehensive and medically relevant. Also, I might do some soft tissue tests and a postural analysis to see where the clients problems lie. Generally it's about talking to a client, seeing why they've come to me and what their problem is. Then I would develop a treatment plan for them and give them a sports massage. Once that's finished, I talk to them and share my findings and my assessment. I may also give them maybe some guidance, some advice on maintenance and a home exercise programme and then we go from there.

What does sports massage involve?

Sports massage is effectively Swedish massage that is applied to issues faced by sportspeople who are recovering from injury, want to prevent injury or as a way of recovering from training and competition. The actual massage is usually a bit harder as more force is applied during the massage strokes. We use a variety of massage techniques, manipulation techniques and stretching to keep muscles healthy and functioning correctly. A lot of the time injured or tight muscles have a restricted blood supply and we apply massage to return the blood supply that brings oxygen and nutrients back to the muscles. This promotes their healing and normal function.

We use massage techniques such as effleurage, petrissage and applying frictions. We also use advanced stretching techniques such as proprioceptive neuromuscular facilitation (PNF) stretches, muscle energy techniques (METs) and post isometric relaxation (PIR) techniques. These techniques can be used to stretch soft tissue, break down scar tissue and reduce tension in the muscles. They can also be used to help improve posture and thus musculoskeletal health.

Who are your clients?

I see a variety of people, from sportspeople to people under 16-years-of-age. Mainly I get middle-aged people who have got postural problems as they have sedentary jobs and are sitting at desks. Most of the time I see back, or back-related problems.

How do you organise your working week?

I'm very mindful about my own health and safety so I will only work a certain number of hours a day. When people start off in this business, they think that they're going to be able to do a full-time sports massage job, but it doesn't always work like that. Sports massage is physical work and you have to look after yourself. There are only so many hours in a day that you can give, and you give fully to your clients, so I do three days a week at the

Woodside Clinic and then half a day at my private practice. I supplement what I do with educational activities, such as teaching and examining. I would do a maximum of 20 hours of massage a week and then spend the rest of the time with less physical work.

Does your work involve evening and weekend work?

Yes, it does involve evenings and weekends and if you want to go into this line of work you have to be flexible. I spent four years working with a rugby team that trained in the evenings and played on Saturday afternoons. I supported them treating injured players during the weekend and then as the First Aider on Saturday. Currently I work in the clinic on evenings and Saturdays and that is really is my bread and butter. You've got to be mindful that people who are working can't get in to see you during the day so they need you to offer evening and weekend appointments.

How did you become qualified as a soft tissue therapist?

I changed my career when I hit 30 as I had been working in banking and computers and I'd got a bit fed up with it. I was interested in sport and had been teaching yoga for a while and I found a lot of people were coming to me with injuries so I decided that I might look at that route. I enrolled on a sports massage therapy course with the London School of Sports Massage.

That took me a year to complete and once I'd completed it, I went part-time with my IT work and built up my work as a sports massage therapist. I did that for two years and then went on to do an advanced diploma in sports therapy with Active Health.

What is the difference between sports therapy and sports massage?

Sports therapy or soft tissue massage is only one aspect of sports therapy. Sports therapy is more complex and includes advanced techniques such as myofascial release and soft tissue manipulation.

What personal skills do you think a good sports therapist needs?

You need to have a warm personality and be able to connect with people. You really do need to have good interpersonal skills and communication is key. In this job you are continually talking to people and sometimes you have to act like a counsellor as people talk about their personal lives. It's quite important because people may have a lot of personal stuff going in their lives on that might give you an indication about the physical state they're in.

Listening skills are important as well as is using visual cues to gauge feedback on the massage. I'm always asking, 'is that all right for you?' or, 'is the pressure okay? We always need to be talking to each other. It's really important to develop the relationship with each client as with a strong relationship comes trust.

Do you think this type of job is easier once you've got a bit of life experience behind you?

Yes, I do and I suppose because I've had a lot of life experience I can adapt to different age groups and can talk about different things. I've developed as a practitioner over 20 years and it took me a couple of years to become confident and comfortable with what I was doing massaging people that came to me.

What advice would you have for people who wanted a similar career to yours?

The first thing that they should do if they want to get into sports massage is to do a short course. Most sports massage schools run a two-day introductory workshop to develop basic massage skills and give people a taste of massage. A lot of people think that massage sounds great but then they find there are barriers because it's a very personal thing that you're doing when you do hands-on work on another person. Let's face it, you're dealing with a naked person and I found when I was teaching students some of them found that really quite difficult to come to terms with. It's beneficial to do an introductory course to see if it's something you are comfortable with. Once you are sure you can deal with it then you can do the sports massage diploma, which is done by attending around 12 weekends over the course of a year, and then slowly build from there.

It's also good experience to work with a sports team or massage at an event like a marathon or triathlon. In my early days I worked with a rugby team and shadowed a physiotherapist. I picked up an awful lot of information just from shadowing the physiotherapist. It's good if you can get work like that, even whilst you're studying, and it helps you build up the massage hours you need to complete your diploma. While you'll do a lot of massage on a course it's worth contacting a cycling team, local football club or a cricket club to give yourself more experience of working in real sporting environments.

You can also study for a degree in sports therapy – what is the difference between doing a diploma and a degree?

Firstly, you would study for three years rather than just one and so will gain more in-depth knowledge. As well as studying sports massage and soft tissue therapy you are likely to learn more about anatomy and physiology. You will also learn more 'sports science' related content such as fundamentals of exercise and movements and using strength and conditioning for rehabilitation. When I was teaching on the foundation degree in sports therapy at Milton Keynes College, we had an open clinic which was fantastic. Students got to experience the practical side and to actually open a clinic up and gain that experience kind of helps you to become the best sports massage therapist really. Also, students will learn about research, how to research and conduct some research themselves. I think you would come out with similar skills for massaging but additional knowledge and skills that you can only develop through degree level study.

What do you enjoy most about your job?

I like the interaction with people and get pleasure when somebody comes to your clinic and they are in pain and discomfort and have maybe lost their range of movement in their neck. I might not be able to fully heal them in one session but at the end of the session if they say they can feel a difference already then that is great. Or they may come back to you a couple of weeks later and say that before they couldn't sleep but now they can – that feels brilliant. It makes you feel like you're doing something worthwhile and that you're making a difference to somebody's life. Some people struggle physically and are in constant pain so you can help them and give them some guidance on exercises and get them thinking a little bit more about the way they sit then that can make a difference to their life. That's what keeps me going really.

What parts of your job do you enjoy less or dislike?

The work can be quite draining physically and mentally, and it takes its toll on your hands and on your back. I make sure that I also have massages and therapy myself. Sometimes you may get difficult cases, for example, I've had a couple of people who start to cry on me. You have to be able to have barriers in place, so you don't take their problems home with you. That can be quite difficult particularly when somebody has opened up to you that they've lost somebody recently and that's why they've come to you. That can be quite a difficult thing to deal with. You need to learn to have coping mechanisms to not take people's problems home with you.

Additional resources

London School of Sports Massage

https://www.lssm.com/index.html

Cambridge School of Sports Massage

http://thecssm.co.uk/

Sports Therapy and Rehabilitation degrees

https://www.whatuni.com/degree-courses/search?subject=sports-therapy

Interview 16

Alistair Bruce-Ball

Sports Broadcaster

Name

Alistair Bruce-Ball

Job title

Sports broadcaster for BBC Radio 5 Live

Qualifications

MA Broadcast Journalism

BA (Hons) Italian and Drama, University of Bristol

Introduction

Alistair Bruce-Ball is a football commentator on BBC Radio 5 Live. He can be heard most weekends commentating on Premiership football. He also commentates on major golf tournaments and The Ryder Cup. Since 2018 he has been the host of 5 Live's football phone in programme '606' with Chris Sutton.

Can you explain how you got into sports broadcasting?

Going right back to the start I was always a huge sports fan as a child. I played everything to a reasonable school level but was never going to be able to play a sport at a professional level. My brother and I were huge sports fans and we always collected football stickers for the World Cups and played football and cricket in the back garden.

However, I did a degree in Italian and Drama at Bristol University which had no relation to sport at all, but I enjoyed languages and I enjoyed acting. You could argue that both these things are valuable to me now as there is a large element of performance in what I do. I got to the last six months of my degree and all my friends were applying for jobs in advertising, marketing or banking while I hadn't given any serious thought to what I actually wanted to do. It was my mum who suggested sports journalism to me. She did all the initial digging around and found some post-graduate broadcast journalism courses.

When I studied broadcast journalism in the mid-90s there were about five or six really good places around the country where you could study for a post graduate degree in broadcast journalism. My initial thought was watching sport for a living and talking about it sounded too good to be true. These courses were not sports journalism courses as they were courses to train to be a journalist and most people went from there on to work in news journalism. When I started looking into getting onto a course I quickly realised that I hadn't really demonstrated any commitment to getting into journalism. There was nothing on my CV that showed I had done any work experience, such as student radio or anything like that. To get some experience I took a year off after university and wrote to hundreds of radio stations, newspapers, television companies but so many replies came back as 'no'. Luckily, I did get the odd one or two that gave me a chance and in particular BBC Radio Bristol said to me 'come in one Saturday afternoon and see what we do'. I did that and a couple of weeks later I got a call from them saying the reporter who was covering the Yeovil Town match on Saturday had fallen sick. They asked me to buy a mobile phone and get down to Huish Park on Boxing Day where I covered Yeovil Town against Bishop Stortford in the Isthmian Premier Division. I used my new phone to do the match report. I'm sure if I listen to those early reports now they would sound dreadful, but they must have been okay as this led me to doing quite a lot of work for BBC Radio Bristol, although it was unpaid. That summer of 1997 I covered Gloucestershire County Cricket Club home and away in the County Championship and I was paid £10 a day. I couldn't afford hotels, so I ended sleeping on friends' floors.

After doing that work experience I reapplied for the post-graduate courses and this time managed to get some interviews. I was offered a place at Cardiff University and studied there for a year from 1997-1998. This course was a stepping stone into journalism because afterwards you were pretty much guaranteed a job in local radio. My goal was to get into journalism, get into a news room and then express my interest in sports journalism. I had always wanted to get into sports journalism as that is where my passion lay. I had to do a general journalism course because there weren't any specialist sports journalism courses then and the basic skills of journalism are the same in whatever field you are reporting in. Those skills are firstly recognising a story and secondly telling that story succinctly.

In June 1998 I started my first full time job at BBC Radio Bristol. At the time they had a three-man sports team but after six months one of the team left and this was when I really got the opportunity to get going with sports reporting. My boss there was Geoff Twentyman, a former Bristol Rovers player, who was a good mentor to me and he felt that I had the skills needed for football commentary. One Friday out of the blue he said to me 'by the way you are doing full commentary on Bristol Rovers versus Notts County tomorrow'. He did this so I didn't have too much time to get nervous about it.

How do you actually learn the skills of football commentary?

I was never really taught how to do commentary and I just had to give it a go and get feedback from people like Geoff and later on my fellow commentators at 5 Live. I learnt from listening to commentators that I actually enjoy listening to and what I think is good commentary and what I think is bad commentary. It's not quite that you copy people's style but you certainly steal the best bits from the broadcasters you like. In terms of specific football commentary schooling, I'm not sure I ever actually had any and I'm not sure anyone actually does.

I worked for three years at BBC Radio Bristol doing football commentary every Saturday, cricket commentary in the summer and some rugby, as in local radio you do a bit of everything. In 2001 a job came up in London at BBC Radio 5 Live and applied for it and got the position. This was working as a bulletin reader, which was actually a step backwards in terms of the commentary I had been doing previously. But I thought that I needed to get onto the bottom rung of the ladder in national radio and then work up from there. I did three years in the role of general sports reporter before getting a job as a full-time football reporter in 2004. In this role I also got the chance to commentate on other sports, such as golf, reporting on the British Open, US Open and The Ryder Cup, which I really enjoy, I've also reported on cricket, rugby and The Olympic Games covering slalom canoeing, cycling, shooting and equestrianism. I've reported on all sorts of sports that I had very little knowledge about.

There is a perception of journalists that you need to pushy and tough minded to be successful. Do you think this is the case?

Funnily enough, before I left school, I did some career analysis and was told exactly the same thing. I was also told I would not be able to work in sales as I wouldn't be ruthless enough to close a deal. It's true that in my line of work there are times when you need a bit of steel such as when you are in a one-to-one post-match interviews with the likes of Pep Guardiola or Jose Mourinho when their team have lost and you have to look them in the eye and ask them hard questions. You try not to be intimidated by them as that is exactly what they are trying to do to you. If they behave unreasonably, as long as you have asked fair questions, then they are the ones who are going to come out looking a bit silly. It can be pretty uncomfortable at the time.

What does a typical working week look like for you?

I do get given a rota for the week ahead I will usually be at matches on Saturday and Sunday. For example, this Saturday I will go to Swansea to report on a match. Reporting is where I give 20 to 30 second updates and report on goals during the full commentary of another match. On Sunday, I will go to Southampton where I will do the full commentary on their match. In the week leading up to the matches I will do a lot of preparatory work on the teams and the players. There is a lot of preparatory work but more so for a commentary match than a reporting one because you won't need as much in-depth knowledge on a reporting game compared to a commentary. Preparing for a commentary match is a full day's work of six to eight hours. I have word document files on all the playing squads but before a match I will update these and transpose the content into hand written notes. I find that when I write by hand the information really goes in. Then I will have Monday and Tuesday off before reporting on Chelsea in the Champions League on Wednesday. Because Chelsea are playing against Roma I will need to do extra preparation on the Roma players as I don't watch them regularly. On Thursday, I will be prepping for a commentary on the Friday night match and then I'll have a reporting game on either Saturday or Sunday. In most weeks I have five days on and two days off, just like in a normal job, but because I am always working at the weekends I get two midweek days off.

From a family point of view this has its pros and cons as working weekends can be tough. I have two boys aged nine and five and they want to know what we are doing at the weekend, but I have to say that I am working. On the other hand, during the week I get to do things such as school runs and taking them to swimming lessons, as I am at home in the week so it does balance itself out a bit.

Which parts of your job do you most enjoy, and which parts do you enjoy less?

I always find that I am wary of grumbling, particularly on air. A lot of people listen to us and might think why on earth are they complaining about their job. In addition to the commentary work I find that our bosses are keen for us to engage with our listeners through social media and take them behind the scenes. For example, we take a picture of where we sit to do the commentary, or show them what the press room is like, and give the listeners an insight into what it is like to cover a game. When we commentate we actually sit out in the stands rather than being tucked away behind glass, so we are exposed to all the elements. If I had any grumbles it would be about the travelling, particularly travelling to and from a midweek game. For example, I might cover a League Cup game that goes to extra-time and penalties and I wouldn't get out of the stadium until around 11 pm and then have a three-hour drive home on the motorway. At the start, I found the travel quite exciting but once you've done it a lot it can become a bit of a grind. But there's not much else I would grumble about.

If you had any advice for any aspiring broadcasters what would that be?

I think if I had my time again I'd do more to get ready and prepare for the career that I wanted. I had a bit of a slow start as I did four years at University, another year gaining unpaid experience, a year doing a post graduate course and another year in local radio, so seven years in total. If I had done more and got some experience at a younger age, I would have got going more quickly. To learn about commentary, you must listen to lots of commentators and commentaries on different sports. Above all you must be yourself and develop your own style. I found that initially 5 Live struggled to find the right place for me and it took me a while to find my feet and establish myself with the listeners. You will notice that each commentator has something distinctive about them. For example, Conor McNamara has a distinctive voice and John Murray has a distinctive style of delivery.

You can try what I did as a child and that is watching sport on television with the sound down and then recording yourself on your phone and listening back to it. It is a brilliant way to practice and learn and you can play it to someone who knows about commentary and they can give you advice and guidance on how to improve. That is a good way to learn. Also, don't get put off by any knock backs you receive, as getting into sports broadcasting is hard and I got so many 'no's' initially before getting in. If you do really want to do it then don't get discouraged and keep plugging away. You almost need to be a nuisance and badger people until they give you a chance.

Also, there are so many different jobs in our department within BBC Radio 5 Live so if you are not the broadcaster, you might be the producer or a researcher. There are researchers who are obsessed by statistics and they put our portfolios about the players in each team together before we go to a World Cup. I had never realised there were so many roles available under the umbrella of sports broadcasting. It is worth researching these opportunities from a young age.

Additional resources

Careers at the BBC

https://careerssearch.bbc.co.uk/

Post graduate degrees in Broadcast Journalism (Cardiff University)

https://www.cardiff.ac.uk/study/postgraduate/taught/courses/course/broadcast-journalism-ma

Interview 17

Adam Leitch

Sports Journalist

Name

Adam Leitch

Job title

Chief Sportswriter at The Daily Echo, Southampton

Qualifications:

National Council for Training Journalists (NCTJ) Diploma

Introduction

Adam is the chief sports writer at the Daily Echo where he has reported on Southampton Football Club matches for over 16 years. He also lectures in Sports Journalism at Southampton Solent University.

How did you get into journalism?

I got into it through a mixture of hard work and luck. I went to college to study for A-levels and thought sports journalism was something I would like to go into. It seemed like it might be quite fun and being from the Southampton region the Daily Echo was my local paper. I came and did some work experience.

You need to bear in mind that now sports journalism is a big industry with numerous sports journalism degree courses. For example, Southampton Solent University has a degree programme with around 100 students coming in a year but when I started out sports journalism wasn't a thing and you couldn't get qualified specifically in it. It was viewed that you went through the traditional route of becoming a news journalist and the sports journalists were not seen as previously being 'proper' journalists. It seems to me that sport is a specialist area of journalism and often it seems that it has overtaken news in importance because of the massive presence of sport online. It is arguably seen to be as big as news so is a speciality now and there are specialist qualifications.

When I came on work experience I was thrown into general news but wanted to work in sport. Afterwards I was able to stay in touch with the paper and got involved in covering Southampton youth football matches for free to get some publications. I was going to study journalism at Bournemouth University and as luck would have it a job became available on the sports desk and after a year I was pretty much a full-time writer. I said I've either got to go to university now or you need to train me, so they put on an NCTJ (National Council for the Training of Journalists) qualification. I was packed off for six months to get qualified and when I came back several of my colleagues had moved on and I was almost last man standing in the sports department at the age of 21. It was more that I happened to be in the right place at the right time that I got to cover Southampton Football Club which was the biggest job on the paper.

Do you think work experience is still important to gain job opportunities?

I lecture at Southampton Solent University as well and always say that if you are really serious about journalism I can't emphasise enough the importance of work experience. I think five of the last six people we appointed had done work experience with us. They are people we know, we know they are good, and we can trust them. If we were advertising for a senior role it may not be the case, but most jobs are entry level roles. We are looking for someone who is enthusiastic and capable so if you have already proved this it puts you in a good position. Even if you are not fortunate that a vacancy comes up during that time then the fact you have been in that environment is very important.

Some people love the environment of the news room while other people are horrified by what it is like, so their experience pays off as they can go away and work somewhere else. You wouldn't buy a car without test driving it first so why would you choose a career before you had tried it out and thrown everything into it? There's nothing worse than studying for three years and finding out you don't want to work in that industry.

How many sports journalists are there at the Daily Echo?

We have five full time members of staff on our sports desk, so we take the bulk of sports coverage and have a few freelancers who have been with us for many years and they cover some of the other things we can't get out to, such as local rugby, cricket and hockey teams. We just don't have the numbers to cover it all. In terms of other sports, we rely on people from the leagues sending reports in. Southampton football, Hampshire cricket and major non-league football clubs are covered by in-house staff.

The impression of journalists can be that you need to be quite pushy to be successful – is this the case?

In my role in the regional press I deal with one football club and that has been central to my working life for 16 years. Being too pushy, annoying, or in your face is not a great way to maintain relationships with contacts. I am reliant on a small pool of people that I deal with on a daily basis. Getting on with people whilst trying to do your job is the balance you are trying to strike. Your personality style has to be that you are friendly, reasonable and approachable to speak to. If you want to discuss something with a contact, you need their trust. If you work for the national press you probably worry less as you are dealing with a number of clubs. You may worry less about upsetting or burning contacts to get a good story. If you are dealing with one club and you upset them then your contacts will dry up fairly quickly.

Can you describe a typical working day?

That is difficult as there are three types of day. Firstly, a day in the office, secondly a day doing pre-match reports and thirdly, a match day and they are all entirely different. We deal with a couple of types of story. There are stories that are event driven such as a game or a quotes piece from someone you have spoken to. That might be a pre-match interview, press conference or post-match interview. That forms the bulk of our stories and these are fairly straightforward. Or there may be a story from a contact that you have to chase and research. These situations can be more complicated when you have to run a difficult story as you want to keep everyone happy – the readers, the paper as well as being fair to the people involved in the story and present it in an appropriate manner. You've got to make sure you have got the facts right and are satisfied it is not a story that will cause you undue problems. If it is going to cause you undue problems you've got to be sure it is worth it.

Is there any other advice you would give to students who want a similar career to yours?

You have to think what it is that you can offer to people that is different. There are so many people coming out with journalism degrees and you need to be able to offer something unique. In your year group there may be 100 other people after the same job as you. You need to be able to show that you understand something in a way that is different to other people. It is an industry where there are jobs, but you need to do something that makes you stand out – what is different about you? This is the first generation of people that have grown up with the internet, social media and mobile phones. Most of the people who employ today's graduates won't understand technology the way you do. The world has changed since those people qualified and have been in the world of work. Young people are much more qualified than they may think as they take it for granted that Google and Facebook have always existed, but we know that they haven't. It means you have a set of skills and instinctive knowledge of technology to utilise and that is where the future lies. There is a greater appetite for good journalism now and a far greater potential audience for journalism thanks to the internet than there has ever been before. So think about things that you can do and specialities that you have. It's great to cover football but everyone wants to cover football, so you may be better off if you know a lot about sailing, motor cycle racing or another niche sport. Think about specialities and niches and be prepared to explore. Make sure you get as much work experience as you can as well as having a degree. A week's work experience is not going to be enough.

What are the parts of your job do you enjoy most and which parts do you enjoy least?

I love being a journalist and am privileged to have met so many interesting people along the way. You have ups and down but it's a fabulous job if you love sport but can't be involved in professional sport. I still love the buzz of going and covering matchday. I must have done 1,000 games, but I still love it and then getting to write about it as well makes it a perfect combination. I love working to deadlines and being under pressure. Also I enjoy getting out of the office, asking people questions, analysing their responses and then voicing my own opinion. People don't always agree with you but it's a privilege to have people listen to you.

The cons are that it is very much a lifestyle job and can be all consuming. You work nearly every weekend, during the holidays at Christmas and New Year and all the other times when people are spending time with friends and family. On Friday or Saturday night you might be driving up to Liverpool rather than seeing your friends. It is a very certain type of lifestyle and is definitely not a Monday to Friday 9 to 5 type of lifestyle. Social media and the internet have made it 24/7 and you have to be able to deal with that. It's not a job that suits everyone and pay in journalism is not great, so you won't have a particularly luxurious lifestyle. The other con is that opportunities are shrinking and there is more focus on productivity and you can get dragged into the office to do jobs like sub editing. There is less opportunity to get out of the office and meet people because you are needed in the office to produce news as there are fewer people. That is a negative with the industry that one of the great things of being a journalist is becoming harder to do.

Additional resources

James Tovey (2013) Sports Journalism – The Inside Track

National Council of Journalism website:

http://www.nctj.com/want-to-be-a-journalist/Sportsjournalism

Sports Journalism courses at Southampton Solent University

https://www.solent.ac.uk/courses/undergraduate/sport-journalism-ba

Interview 18

Vicki Galvin

Sport and Physical Activity Manager

Name

Vicki Galvin

Job title

Sport and Physical Activity Manager at Oxford City Council

Qualifications

BA(Hons) Dance Performance, Middlesex University

Premier Diploma in Personal Training

Introduction

Vicki works for Oxford City Council as a sport and physical activity manager developing the opportunities in the city. This involves working on building facilities, promoting activities in schools and communities and engaging less active groups. She also teaches fitness classes in her spare time.

What do the City Council do in relation to sport and physical activity?

Within my team we oversee sports and physical activity for city. We look after facility developments as we've got a capital grant programme where we build facilities. For example, we're working on a £5m development at Horspath at the moment where we're building a brand-new sports complex in partnership with Oxford United and BMW. We're resurfacing five of our outdoor tennis courts and installing new floodlights. We work in partnership and support other development projects that are going to generate better resources and facilities for the communities that we work within. We also have a remit within schools.

We have an officer who works with all the primary and secondary schools in the city to support them on spending their primary school premium package that they have ring-fenced from the government. This has recently been increased as a result of the sugar levy. The schools have more money ring-fenced for physical education and we have a package that they can spend that on. That is with Create Development who run Real Play, Real Coaching, Real PE. We deliver those courses to train teachers across the city and hopefully embed those skills within schools so that they can sustain their own physical education curriculum. We train primary school teachers to gain swimming qualifications so they can support or lead lessons for their children. The aim is for every year six child to leave primary school being able to swim.

We deliver countywide projects for the city which are sometimes funded by Sport England and sometimes by the Clinical Commissioning Group (CCG). This could be engaging our inactive demographic or focusing on women and girls. We're currently about to launch a project around diabetes to involve pre-diabetics and diabetic patients.

What does your job entail on a daily basis?

My job is a management role around the strategic direction of the team and linking that in to other local and national strategies. I work with our county council, our partners in health, our County Sports Partnership, and then link to the Department of Culture, Media and Sport (DCMS) and Sport England strategies, ensuring there's that golden thread through to our leisure and wellbeing strategy. I ensure we are working to meet our team plan and therefore our leisure and wellbeing strategy and partner strategies as a result. So a lot of work is around partnership development and relationship development.

I manage a team of five people and then we have our instructors and volunteers, so it's about 40 staff that work on our programmes,

Tell me about your qualifications

I did A-levels in Dance because that was my passion, English and Psychology and Geography and then I did my degree which was a BA (Hons) in Dance Performance at Middlesex University. I loved doing my degree but looking back maybe I could have done something different but I would have regretted not following what my passion was at that time. During that time we had various fitness modules because if you're dancing six or seven hours a day you've got to be fit, and it can't just be achieved through dancing. We had modules on fitness modules, anatomy and physiology and I started to get interested in fitness.

Up until that point I'd just been dancing, and if you asked me to go for a run or go and do some weights or pull-ups I'd have said 'no way!'. But I started seeing the benefits of it and then I started to enjoy it a lot more. At the start of my degree if you'd said you're going to leave this course and have an interest in fitness I wouldn't have believed you. But when I left university I decided I wasn't going to pursue dance but work with my interest around fitness.

That's when I went to Premier Training to do my Diploma in Personal Training and tried to do every add-on course that I could, such as ultrasound, taping and strapping. From there I sent letters out to various sports clubs and contacted my local leisure centre. I managed to get myself into a position where I was volunteering to do sports massage for my local rugby club. And that's given me some great experience in sports therapy. I ended up being there for seven or eight years working with Chinnor Rugby Club. That was fantastic because I learnt the therapeutic and injury rehab side of things. Also, it was great to be part of a sports team.

I also got part-time work as a gym instructor at the local leisure centre in Thame. They couldn't offer me full-time work, so I got qualified to teach circuit training, body combat and spinning to help fill the time and bring my wages up. When they offered me a full-time position, I actually didn't have time to take it. I was so busy by that point as I'd started personal training and sports massage as well.

After three or four years one of my friends, who was a master trainer for a company who make indoor spinning bikes and fitness equipment, persuaded me to meet their MD. She was one of their master trainers for the UK and they needed someone to help out with training. I think I talked myself into a job even though he wasn't sure whether there was even a role. I became their UK training and education manager and would go around and train people how to use their equipment. I developed the modules they delivered and got them accredited with CPD points. I worked with YMCA and various sports clubs.

I spent three years covering the whole of the UK by myself. Maybe I had shot myself in the foot by just agreeing to everything and being quite good at the things that they asked me to do. But the MD would ask me to do more and more. It got to the point where I was delivering the training, I was selling the training, I was developing the training, I was presenting and there was a lot of travelling involved and it just wasn't for me. I got to the point where I wasn't getting job satisfaction because I was so worn out. At this point a job had come up as Go Active Coordinator for Oxford City Council.

It was coordinating a physical activity project which is still in place and something I work on now. It felt like it combined the personal training skills that I'd built up, as well as some of the skills that I'd learnt from my time in my previous role - those management, marketing and communication skills. So it just seemed like it was a nice blend of them both and was still out and about but just round Oxford rather than the UK.

Then two years ago I was promoted to sport and physical activity manager to manage the team that I was a part of. And I think that journey has given me a good insight into what it's like to be out there delivering services to meet the needs of communities, through to how projects work and how they develop.

I understand the people that I manage because I've done one of their roles. So I actually have an understanding of what's involved in their roles. Whilst I want them to shape their roles in a way that suits them the environment that they're working in is constantly changing I know. There is pressure that they are under and barriers that they are coming up against and I can support them with that.

What is it about your job that you enjoy and don't enjoy?

I started with a huge passion for sport and I still absolutely have that. I still keep myself fit and healthy and we're big advocates of mental wellbeing and obviously physical activity is a way to support your own mental wellbeing. Running and teaching my classes is how I look after my mental health. But my day-to-day job is less about sport and physical activity now but I still have that connection to sport and physical activity and that will never go. But what I love about my job now isn't necessarily solely around sport and physical activity. I love building partnerships with people. I've been told that my communication skills are very strong so hopefully I'm putting those to good use.

I love that we can be innovative and creative and think outside the box to find solutions. We work in partnership with different departments and actually provide a better service, a better experience and have more impact around health and wellbeing and sport and physical activity than if we were working alone.

There are some elements of my job I don't like. In any job there's going to be difficult relationships and difficult conversations to be had. Sometimes working for a council can feel like there are too many cooks involved. But I like to see these things as challenges rather than negatives. As a manager I'm now a little bit removed from the actual doing of activities, and when you're doing that you get that instant feedback, such as 'that session was great' which gives you instant job satisfaction. I was a bit concerned that I was going to be removed from that and whether I would get job satisfaction doing this job. It was something that I had lost when working in my previous role and was why I left ultimately.

What advice would you have for people who are starting off studying sport now who want to get into your type of work?

I'm probably echoing what other people have said but it is so important to gain experience. We have a number of volunteering opportunities and offer work experience. Putting those hours in to gain experience, obviously looks great in terms of your commitment but also it might help shape your vision of what you want to do exactly. Local authorities do have a lot of opportunities and they're not as dull and boring as people think. As well as the benefits of flexibility and a supportive environment around health and wellbeing there are good structures in place in terms of your pension and your own personal development.

I'd say gain some experience, develop your skillset because there are a lot of transferable skills you will develop in our industry. Skills such as project management, communication skills, developing partnerships and relationship building. They can come from any other industry but working in sport and physical activity can definitely help to develop these.

What are the possibilities for promotion and development working for a council?

If someone came to work in our city council they could start off as a lifeguard in a leisure centre and move up to become a duty manager. I started as a coordinator, moved into a permanent role, and then into a management position.

My line manager started off as a lifeguard and he's worked at the city council for 25 years. He now manages the whole of Active Community overseeing all the community centres, the green spaces, the youth ambition team and the leisure contracts. All from starting work as a lifeguard.

Additional resource

Oxford City Council Sport and Physical Recreation

https://www.oxford.gov.uk/info/20230/sports_development/785/sports_development_team

Interview 19

Nik Elphick

Sports Equipment Sales

Name

Nik Elphick

Job title

Regional Sales Manager for SportsArt

Qualifications

Premier Diploma in Personal Training

BTEC National Diploma in Sports Coaching

Introduction

Nik works selling fitness training equipment to gyms, personal fitness studios and schools across the south of England. He has previously been a gym manager and a personal trainer.

What is your current job?

I am regional sales manager for SportsArt in the south of England. I cover everything to the south of Loughborough. Although predominantly it's a sales role, I am also an account manager. I manage the accounts of customers across the south of England that have our fitness equipment. I am responsible for approaching fitness club owners and developing new business. I spend a lot of time with current customers building up relationships by having lunch or coffee with them.

What is SportsArt?

We provide fitness equipment, treadmills, exercise cycles and weight training equipment that is innovative and durable but also is good for the environment as the energy produced during training is then returned to the facility's electrical grid. In this way the provider saves money as well as contributing to sustainability of the planet.

What does your job entail on a daily basis?

I spend around three days a week driving around the south of England visiting gyms. I visit independent clubs which are so fascinating, because there's so many different types, even down to personal trainers promoting facilities that they work from. I also visit big chains like Nuffield Health, as well as hospital gyms and school gyms.

When I go to a gym it is not just about selling equipment as I'll help them to change their layout and I'll say this piece of equipment would look great over here. I get involved in everything as I use my sales experience and industry experience to help them develop marketing and membership sales. For example, at the moment I am working with a school helping them to do a marketing plan to get more members. I'll say that 'if you're looking to spend £30,000 on new equipment, you'll need this many new members each paying a certain amount, and this is how you could get those new members'. I point out what their key selling points are and what campaigns might work, like 'Bring a Buddy Fridays'. I'm as much an adviser as well as a key account sales manager.

Tell me about your qualifications

At school I got several GCSEs with Bs and Cs. Once I left school, I did a two-year sports coaching course at Park House College in Newbury. It was aimed at footballers and it gave you your UEFA B football coaching qualification as well as a BTEC in Sports Coaching. I also did my National Pool Lifeguard Qualification and then went on to do the Premier Diploma in Personal Training.

How did your career develop from there?

I went to work at the Spirit Club within The Holiday Inn Hotel in Oxford. I worked as a gym instructor and then became assistant manager after they put me on a management course. The reason I went there was to get experience of every aspect of working in and managing a gym. I learnt about finance, managing memberships, sales, and working in the gym doing inductions and taking classes. And how to operate the pool. I got to work with every aspect of health and fitness club operations and after 18 months I got promoted to club manager which I did for a couple of years before spending a year travelling. I went to Australia and got a job at Fitness First as a sales consultant. That is where I got a passion for sales. I was still working in the gym environment, but I was selling memberships to people. I was using my knowledge and experience of fitness to sell memberships by relating to people telling them what they needed to do to lose weight or build up their body. When I came back to England, I got a job in membership sales at what was Esporta in Oxford (now Nuffield Health) and I've worked in sales ever since.

I always found that selling was quite easy. I always found out what triggered the person to come in and have a look around the gym. They always come in for a reason. Whether it's because they're getting married, they've had a health scare or they're just unhappy with how they're feeling at the moment. Then I relate that trigger back to what resources we have in the gym, the swimming pool, the spa, or the tennis courts. They may be a bit lonely and want to meet new people. I try to relate to people and build a relationship with them using my selling techniques.

How do you go about building the relationship between yourself and a customer?

I think it is predominantly down to personality but because everyone is different there are some people that you won't have a connection with or be able to build rapport with. I use my personality and try to find some common ground between us. The key for me is to build a relationship with a person before I try and sell to them. At the moment I'm working with a school and I've got a lot of competition because they'd just had funding for almost £200,000. Now all the big players are getting involved as they've started seeing that there's potential to get some sales. But I've developed a relationship with that school by going down there regularly and help them to do things for charity. I also cover classes for them and I was down there yesterday, so I popped in for a cup of tea and I was there for about an hour helping them move boxes around.

Where did you go after working at Esporta?

I stayed in selling but moved into the motor trade thinking it might work out as a long-term career. I got a job in selling working for Mercedes Benz and I saw that most sales people were in their 40s and 50s. So my thinking was I can go into this role and I can stay in this role for 20 years. I can do my training in my own time, before work or after work I'll be in a role where I'll feel safe for the long term, until I retire. I was in it for six months. I did really well in those six months, but I didn't like it because I missed the fitness industry totally. I missed the environment. I didn't like working in an environment where they ate doughnuts, worked long hours without breaks. They weren't interested in nutrition and instead of having a lunch break, they'd go out for a cigarette or have a cup of coffee. They'd get doughnuts and pizzas brought in and it just wasn't the environment I was comfortable working in. I'd sit in the canteen eating a salad or a chicken breast with some rice and they'd all take the mick out of me.

I wasn't passionate about cars either. I like cars but I didn't feel passionate when I was trying to sell one to someone. I'd say this is a £70,000 car, lovely leather interior, heated seats and steering wheel but it was so dull as it meant nothing to me. I wasn't as passionate about it as I was about fitness. So I left there to get a job with SportsArt. And I've done this role for a year now and it's probably the most enjoyable role I've been in since I was in Australia.

You've also worked as a personal trainer – what did you learn during that time?

If I could change one thing about working as a PT it would be that after completing my qualification, I'd pick one area to specialise in. Personal training is such a broad field and there so many different types of clients. I wanted to do everything. I wanted to do strength and conditioning training, bodyweight training, spinning and circuits classes, working with medical conditions, GP referrals and cardiac rehabilitation. I didn't have a passion for one area in particular. I should have focused on one area and that should have been medical conditions, working with special populations and exercise as rehabilitation. Because I'm diabetic I've got an insight into diabetes so I could have worked with Type 1 and Type 2 diabetics who train after a GP referral.

I could see other personal trainers that specialised in one area becoming very good in that area and because they were successful people would go to them for that reason. Once they had enough experience they would start branching off and set up their own businesses based on their specialism. That might be exercise rehabilitation, posture and flexibility, training for running, martial arts or boxing. There are so many different things that personal trainers can do. It is important to get some experience first in a gym and then after a couple of years you can specialise.

Which of the parts of your job that you like, and which are those you dislike?

The hardest thing about my current job is the lack of awareness of the product I am selling. People haven't heard of the brand and if you're trying to sell something people haven't heard of, you have to work that bit harder to get people to buy into the product and become interested in it. Also being a newish company you do have to do a lot of ground work like knocking on doors, going to places uninvited, cold calling and that can be uncomfortable. That would probably be the trickier part of the job.

I love my role because it has variety. Some days I go to gyms and meet new people. Other days I have an admin day working from home. I do site visits and develop plans for gyms. I talk to people about how they're going to have their gyms laid out, what equipment they need based on what their plans for their membership, the demographic of their members and their long-term goals.

I love being in the fitness industry and learning about facilities and about trends in the fitness industry - what's happening and what's going to happen.

And what about your future, have you got opportunities for career development?

As we are a new company, we've got a team of only six people in the UK at the moment. I cover the whole of the south, someone else covers the whole of the north of England. There's a national manager who oversees our work and manages the office. We've got a Product and Service manager for the UK and three staff that work in the office. As the company grows, we'll get more staff as the number of accounts increases. There'll be key account manager and sales director roles created. My short-term aim is to get our eco-power range in as many facilities as I can. For example, we're currently negotiating to work with a big budget chain and that would be a massive account. As the company develops my role will change and hopefully, I'll end up managing a team of people like myself. My goal within the next five years is to become a sales director for the south. One of the benefits of being with a new company at the start is that your role grows and develops as the company grows.

Interview 20

Grace Kelly

Outdoor Pursuits Instructor

Name

Grace Kelly

Job title

Senior Outdoors Activity Instructor

Qualifications

BTEC Level 3 Sport (Outdoor Pursuits)

Introduction

Grace is a Senior Instructor at Standon Bowers Outdoor Education Centre, which is in the Midlands and is part of Entrust.

What does your job entail on a daily basis?

I lead and instruct outdoor activities for young people of all ages. We normally work with school children from Year 2 up to Year 6 which is eight-year olds up to 12-year olds. The activities we offer include rock climbing, BMX biking, kayaking and in the summer, canoeing. We also take the children scrambling, which is climbing across rough or steep ground. We get them to put on helmets and go off and have an adventure with them. I am responsible for the safety of these children and ensuring that the activities are carried out within health and safety regulations.

In the summer we have students from the National Citizen Service (NCS) which is for 16 to 18-year olds. They sign up for four weeks in the summer holidays and spend one of those weeks with us. They come from all over the country but mainly from East and West London. It is great to work with this different age group and they have completely different experiences to what they are used to. They are used to the city environment and we show them what they can do in the countryside.

The young people come for a week and because it is residential, I do have to work at least one evening a week or even overnight. Usually my hours are 9 am to 5 pm but if I do an overnight shift, I would leave work at 5 pm the next day.

Tell me about your education and how your career has developed

At school I didn't know what I wanted to do and lacked any real direction, but I was always passionate about the outdoors. I grew up in an area called Cannock Chase so spent a lot of time riding my bike in the forest, building shelters and jumping in muddy puddles. I saw this course at Stafford College which was Outdoor Adventure Sports and it sounded perfect to me. So I did two years at college studying for a BTEC National Diploma in Outdoor Sports and at the same time I did work experience at an Outdoor Pursuits Centre. But I wasn't a very outgoing person and found it difficult to talk to groups. The scariest thing for me was having to talk to a group of 16 kids. However, for this work experience I had to come out of my comfort zone and stand up in front of groups and lead them.

The experiences I had over two years really built my confidence up and I became used to talking to groups. At the end of the two years the business I was volunteering for offered me a summer job so I worked there for the summer; however, I couldn't get any work there for the winter season, so I went to work in bars and restaurants just to get me through. I then reapplied to the company and got work in the summer season and have never left.

At college I struggled to sit still all day in a classroom or in front of a computer so I knew that I could never work indoors in an office job. Part of my job is to complete paperwork such as risk assessments and accident report forms, but once I finish, I know I can go outside and get on a bike or clamber across rocks, get absolutely drenched and come back and have a shower and a hot chocolate. In the summer it is just the best job in the world, particularly when the sun shines and you are outside inspiring kids and having fun.

During my time at college the tutors got us working outside and that really inspired me. Many of my tutors also found it difficult to be in a classroom and wanted to be outside. They would tell us about their adventures and what they got up to at the weekends on their mountain bikes or climbing up mountains.

What other qualifications have you got to lead outdoor activities?

I have several National Governing Body awards. For climbing I have the mountain training award, for paddling I have Level 1 Canoe and Kayak award which allows me to run sessions in sheltered water under supervision, I have an archery instructor award, climbing wall and abseiling award which is for indoor climbing walls. I have just competed the rock climbing instructors award so I can go out on natural crags and take a group of eight children climbing and abseiling for the day. I've done my local mine leader award which means I can take children exploring underground for the day. We have an old copper mine nearby and we explore the old underground mines and the waterfalls. I have a hill and moorland leader award which means I can take groups walking in areas such as the Peak District. I also have a first aid qualification which is tailored to working outdoors.

In addition to these awards I have done a sign language course. We work a lot with a charity called Sense, which is for deaf and blind children. The sign language course enables me to communicate with them more effectively.

In your job what personal skills do you think are most important?

Because we deal with customers face to face, we have to be very professional in our approach. Our customers are the teachers who bring the groups as well as the young people themselves. We need to be role models to the young people we work with as they will look up to us. A lot of these young people see adults on reality programmes, such as Geordie Shore or Love Island, and they are often their role models. We need to show them that you don't have to wear lots of make-up and have work done on your face to be a really good person. You can look natural and just be yourself.

When working with young people we always set boundaries for behaviour early on, so they know what they can and cannot do. This helps to build the relationship between us and them and once we can trust them, we can get to know them better. We have to be really adaptable according to our type of audience and you can't always be nice as sometimes you have to change roles and be really tough. At times you need to be like their mum and other times like their head teacher, particularly when you are setting boundaries.

When I started working aged 18, I didn't have a clue about how to deal with people but working in bars and restaurants really helped me get used to the general public. One big thing I learnt is that it is often easier to agree with people rather than argue or try to reason with them.

In my role I have to be so adaptable in how I deal with people. It is particularly challenging working with blind and deaf children; for example, when you take them out canoeing and they can't necessarily hear or see you. It can be really dangerous if you are unable to communicate with them at all. I also work with children with special education needs (SEN) and always try to change my language and make it clear and understandable to them. With blind children I have to use more descriptive language and when working with deaf children it is important to be in a position where they can always see me. I sometimes get confused with how some younger people talk and the different meanings that they give to words. For example, 'sick' means something good rather than bad so you have to keep up with the young people's language. Communication is often about trying to understand what the other person is saying or means.

Which parts of your job do you most enjoy, and which parts do you enjoy less?

The parts I really enjoy are taking children to some gorgeous places that are on their doorstep but because they are so busy on mobile phones and playing games, they don't open their eyes to them and the thrills they can have. The outdoors is like a big play park that is available to them for free and if they have a bike and a helmet they can go and have their own adventures. I get a real kick out of inspiring young people and introducing them to new experiences. I also love being outside myself and I never really feel uncomfortable when I am wet as I know before long I'll be dry and warm again.

The part I least enjoy is when young people don't enjoy being outdoors as they are so used to being inside and playing computer games. They complain about getting filthy or having dirty hands and they often don't like hard work. I think it is good for them to get dirty and feel uncomfortable for a time. We also have to do a good deal of paperwork, such as accident reports, even when someone gets a small cut and you have to put on a plaster.

There aren't any parts of my job that I dislike. I get up every morning and absolutely love going to work and there's not many people that can say that.

What advice would you have for someone who wanted a similar career to yours?

You need to make sure you have your own adventures so that you know how young people might be feeling when they are hanging off a cliff or abseiling down it. You need to know what it feels like to be scared so that you can relate to how other people are feeling. If you are not sure whether it is a career for you then go and do some work experience and you will soon find if you like being outside all day, sometimes in the dark and in horrible weather.

To gain experience I did Camp America and had the best summer of my life as a mountain bike instructor in the Rocky Mountains. This job does give you that flexibility where you can go and work in America for a summer or be a ski instructor for the winter. You really can travel with this job and see new places. When I got to Camp America, I already had experience as a mountain bike instructor and as a result none of my groups suffered any serious injuries while people in groups with less experienced instructors were getting broken bones and other serious injuries. It's all about group management and you can't learn that from a book – you've got to get out and find out what works and what doesn't work.

What are the opportunities for your career development?

Since we were taken over by Capita the business has grown and grown. We now take on groups for their Duke of Edinburgh award. I am currently a senior instructor, but I could become chief instructor where I would have a team of 10 instructors and be responsible for their development and make sure they have all the training and resources that they need. After that I could be a centre manager which is less hands on and making sure all users are safe by doing risk assessments and making sure the building is safe. Or I could change my line of work and become a first aid trainer or go to work at head office and work in sales and marketing. There are so many opportunities in this line of work. Maybe in the outdoor industry progression is slower because you need to spend time as an instructor getting experience, so you understand the industry. We are taking people out onto mountains and if we have a bad day someone could get killed so you need a base of knowledge to keep people safe.

If I was to move up, I would take a step back from working with young people and maybe one day that will suit me. The time is going to come when my knees hurt or my back hurts, but I've got too much energy right now.

Additional resources

Entrust

https://www.entrustoutdoors.co.uk/

National Citizenship Service

https://www.gov.uk/government/get-involved/take-part/national-citizen-service

Chapter 3 - How to give yourself the best chance for a successful career in sport

Introduction

In this chapter we are going to look at what else you need, apart from your degree, to give yourself the best opportunity to be successful in your career and crucially to stand out from the crowd. As we said earlier, there are around 15,000 graduates each year from sports science and sports related courses and an additional 1200 postgraduates who are qualified to master's degree or PhD level. There are a limited number of jobs for this huge pool of graduates so for you to gain an interview will have to be able to offer something special that differentiates you from other candidates.

Firstly, you will need as good a degree as possible and ensure that you have a well-rounded and well-developed knowledge of all areas covered by your degree. But remember that so many other graduates will have this as well. In this chapter we will focus on the role of personal skills and their vital importance to your future career. We will look at what these personal skills are, why degree level study may not fully develop the personal skills that you need, and how you can work on them during your time as a student.

Degree level study may not equip you with all the skills that you need to work effectively in sport and fitness environments

Universities possess expertise in setting up opportunities for learning and developing your knowledge. They have highly qualified lecturers who are familiar with the latest research and theory and they can guide you towards the right resources to develop your knowledge. They are also excellent in teaching about research and supervising your own research projects, as well as developing your skills of criticality so that you can challenge what you are learning. Most universities have high class facilities where you can see knowledge put into practice, and excellent sports facilities to give you practical experience and develop your own sporting skills.

Universities are also tasked with developing what are referred to as employability skills. These are a set of skills or attributes that you will need to become effective in your working role in the future. Universities deliver these by embedding skills in the delivery and assessment of the knowledge they teach, creating opportunities to specifically work on these skills and offering work experience or industrial placements. Universities can teach employability skills in a general way, but they may not be able to differentiate enough and teach skills specific to each role. For example, the personal skills to be an effective sport psychologist will differ from those needed to be a strength and conditioning coach.

Universities may struggle to offer authentic, real life situations for you to develop personal skills. This is particularly the case when we look at the demands of high performance or elite sport. Performance sports environments can be highly pressurised, complex environments which are constantly changing, and an individual's weaknesses or deficiencies can be cruelly exposed. This unique environment can accentuate the gap between the skills that are needed to be successful and those skills graduates actually possess. To address this many universities have links to professional sports clubs who offer internships. Internships usually last one year and they provide students with access to working with professional athletes. This type of experience is so valuable to undergraduate students and can lead to full time work.

Steve Ingham is the Director of Supporting Champions, which he has set up to develop the skills of practitioners working in performance sport. Every academic year Steve produces a blog titled 'A letter to the 15,000' which refers to the 15,000 sports science students who graduate each year, and in particular those who aspire to work in performance sport. He produces this as a result of his frustration about the gap that exists between what performance sport requires from professionals and the skills that graduates actually possess when they leave university. In 2018 I spoke to Steve and he summarised the problem:

> "I have been working on this issue for 15 years and the gap is not narrowing between what is required to work in sport and what is taught on degrees. The pressures are rising, and the expectations are going up. There has been a worsening of skill level in graduates coming out of the higher education sector. In my experience of interviewing scientists and medics working in performance sport I think it is getting worse. This is based on over 500 interviews across 20 years.
>
> The crunch point for me was in 2008, after the Beijing Olympics, when I was Head of Physiology. I was receiving calls from coaches, such as David Brailsford, and they were saying 'I don't want this person on my team, they don't know how we work, they don't work well with the team and I can't have that.' I would ask what is it are they not doing? Are they not knowledgeable enough or do they not have the right procedures or analysis methods?' Time and time again in the vast majority of cases the answer was a flat 'no'. The response was that the problem was all behavioural and related to the individual's skill or craft. They had annoyed the coach at the

wrong time, just when the pressure was on and when the team dynamic relied on people pulling in the same direction. Their communication was poor, they were too standoffish, they had negative body language, or they stepped over a line.

In a podcast titled 'Steve Ingham on developing performance people' (2019) Steve explains that sports scientists have to have the ability to:

"Work with other people, to work between the edges in the messy, ambiguous world of high-performance sports where their character and professional craft really gets exposed."

Steve's philosophy is that if we expect our athletes to be high performing (and we do) then they must expect to have a high-performance team around them. In British sport over the last 20 years we have done everything we can do to ensure that athletes have the right environment around them to be successful. They have the funding they need, the access to excellent facilities, outstanding coaching and medical support, but we have not invested in the support team around them in the same way. The support team have the knowledge, but they don't necessarily have the skills or craft needed.

The importance of personal or craft skills to employers is growing as well. Exercise physiologist, Luke Gupta, explained to me about how employers make decisions about who they employ based on their personal skills rather than their knowledge:

There was a time when an employer looked for the most qualified person on paper thinking that the softer skills would be developed along the way. Now it is almost the other way around, as employers look for good people who will fit in with their culture knowing they can teach them the technical skills. Working with people is about getting on with them and while good communication and good listening are important if you can get on with the coach and the athletes in a sport you are going to be successful.

Ideally, this development of craft skills needs to begin when you start your studies aged 16 or 18 not once you have started working.

Working with people in sports environments is problematic and challenging!

As obvious as it may sound, the big issue when you work in sport or fitness environments is that you are invariably going to end up working with other human beings. This may be on a one-to-one basis, such as in the personal training situation, leading a small or large group of people, such as when you are coaching a group, or working as part of a team, for example a multidisciplinary team supporting performance athletes. These situations all involve human interaction, and this is where things can becomes problematic. By nature situations that involve other people can be complex as there can be many variables at play.

All situations involving human interaction will involve relationships, or a network of relationships, that need to be initiated, developed, nurtured and maintained. Working with other people is difficult because people are ever changing and relationships tend to be unstable, unpredictable and complex. You will have to deal with different personalities and personalities that change dependent on their mood, emotional state and differing motivations which may also change daily. You will have to deal with the situations that other people find themselves in and the positive and negative experiences that they go through.

When we study we can learn knowledge quite quickly, and we often find that we have 'Eureka moments' where we make a sudden breakthrough that enables us to understand concepts such as how the energy systems resynthesise ATP or how osteoblasts build new bones. However, our personal skills are related to our personality and our behaviour, so changing either of these can be more difficult. The development of personal skills is a slow and gradual process in contrast to the more immediate learning of knowledge. It also takes a specific type of learning for us to explore our experiences and assess our own strengths and weaknesses. This type of learning is referred to as reflective learning.

Ian McEwan in his book *Machines Like Me* describes how you can teach a machine to play chess and beat human beings because chess has set rules, each piece can move but it moves are pre-defined, so it always moves in certain, set ways. Chess is a closed system that is predictable, unlike life where we have to learn how to operate in an open system. We are asked to apply our intelligence and use our skills in an unpredictable environment that McEwan (2019) describes as being:

"Messy, full of tricks and feints and ambiguities and false friends." (p.178)

We are given language to help us navigate through this open system, but language is also open to interpretation and thus often unreliable.

We can be taught about personal skills, but we will only truly learn from experiencing situations where our skills are engaged and tested, and this is what our studies at college and universities have to do. However, learning about human interaction and developing relationships takes a lot of time and experience. Later in this chapter you will find out about opportunities within your studies that you can use to prepare for working with other people and working as part of a team.

What personal skills do you need to develop to prepare for working in sport?

It seems that when working in sport and fitness the most important thing is being able to develop relationships, because once you have a relationship you can start to gain the trust of another person. Chris Barry, the sports analyst, describes how he needs to have strong relationships within his multidisciplinary team so that when he speaks what he says makes an impact. He suggests that the relationship is the 'glue' that binds what he says to how it is received. Laura Heathcote, the physiotherapist describes how building relationships with coaches is important for the times when she needs to influence a situation or when she is suggesting a specific course of action for an athlete. She also says that the relationship with her athletes is crucial to ensuring that they complete their rehabilitation programmes because if they don't trust you then they won't do it. Sport and exercise psychologist, Sarah Murray says a similar thing that if you get the relationship part right with other people then you can start talking to them about the science part and they will take the information on board. Football coach, Richard Horner, explains how without a strong relationship you will never get to a point where you can address the aspects of an athlete's performance that you need to, or have the difficult conversations that may be required. In the tough world of sports journalism Adam Leitch describes how relationships are important so that your contacts, football managers and players, will talk to you and divulge information. This has to be balanced against doing your job well and presenting information that may not always be in those people's interests.

These reasons show the importance of being able to develop relationships so that people trust you and then you can start influencing the other person and getting them to take on board what you are saying to them. A key sign that you have an effective relationship is when other people come to you to ask for your opinion or advice.

Earlier Steve Ingham made the point about some staff annoying the coach, communicating poorly and having poor body language. These factors were clearly impacting on the relationship and the team dynamic. In fact, the way they behaved was destructive to the team and could potentially have impacted on performance.

Exercise physiologist, Emma Ross, describes the key to influencing performance as knowing when to step forward and knowing when to sit back and keep quiet, even when you can see things are going wrong. Building on this, two of the most important things when working with and influencing other people are:

What you say, how you say it and when you say it.

What you do, how you do it and when you do it.

These may look to be simple enough statements but because everyone is an individual with different personalities and because every situation is different you will continually have to be able to adapt what you say and how you act. To get what you say and what you do right (in as many situations as you can) you will need a whole raft of other skills.

Evidently communication skills are key to what you are saying but central to the process of working with other people is self-awareness. Self-awareness is described by Kyndt and Rowell (2012) as the ability to understand your own values, personality, emotions and motives. This will enable you to understand the impact of what you do and say on other people. Kyndt and Rowell (2012) stress that increased self-awareness helps you to manage your emotions and behaviours but also to understand other people better and have empathy with them. If we can understand other people, and their experiences, then this in turn helps us to communicate more effectively with them and develop better relationships. In turn, low self-awareness results in a gap between how you see yourself, what you say and do, and how other people see you and interpret your words and actions. You can see how this would impact negatively on the relationships you develop, and the trust other people will have in you.

In order to be able to develop relationships effectively and influence other people you will also need varying degrees of the following personal skills:

Self-awareness
Communication
Listening
Empathy
Judgement
Emotional intelligence
Creativity/innovation
Adaptability

Every exchange you have with another person, every time you act and speak will be influenced by these skills along with your knowledge and previous experiences. These personal skills warrant individual attention so we will look at each one individually before looking at how they can be developed.

Communication

Communication is described by sports analyst, Chris Barry, as how you deliver information. But there is also an element of how you receive information. He finds that communication is central to his role of working with coaches, as the coach will ask for something specific to be analysed and he needs to ensure they are explicit in their request, so he fully understands it. If he produces the wrong information then it will damage their relationship and waste everyone's time. Inferring things or making assumptions can be major blocks to communication as these inferences or assumptions may not be correct. Chris makes the important point that people will communicate in different ways and that you need to be creative when sending your message so that it lands with impact.

Strength and conditioning coach, Will Abbott, discusses the importance of being able to communicate at different levels, or to people with different levels of maturity and education. In his role he may deliver information to football coaches, some who may have sports science or coaching degrees, and some who may not. He may talk differently to medical staff than to coaches and even the players when discussing their injuries. Will works with different age groups of players from under-9s up to under-23s and there is a huge difference in the language, tone and pace needed to communicate with these groups. Performance nutritionist, Emma Gardner explains that her biggest challenge is putting the amazing knowledge that she has to athletes in a meaningful way so that they can understand it, or else her work will have no impact on their nutritional strategies.

Adapting your language for specific groups is central to effective communication. Sports broadcasting and journalism are both based on communicating with the general public. Sports commentators, such as BBC Radio 5 Live's Alistair Bruce-Ball, only has the spoken word to convey something as visual as football while journalist Adam Leitch can only use the written word. On top of this they have to ensure that their communication is accessible and attractive to specific groups of people. Alistair says that initially 5 Live struggled to place him suggesting they weren't sure what type of people, or sports, his communication style was best suited to.

Outdoor pursuits instructor, Grace Kelly, has found that she has to make major adaptations in her communication style so that she can understand other people and so that they can understand her. In her role, effective communication is central to the safety of her customers. She discusses the challenges of taking hearing impaired students canoeing and ensuring that she is always positioned so that her face can be seen, thus allowing students to lip read. She adapts her language for visually impaired students by using more descriptive language to develop images for them. She also makes the point that words often mean more than one thing or that their meaning changes depending on the context or who is using it. For example, words such as 'sick' can mean something that is very good, a medical condition, or something that is in bad taste.

Communication is about choosing your words carefully so that other people understand them but there are other factors that affect their impact. Our body language, eye contact, facial expressions and gestures all have an impact on how our words are received by another person. If we are not fully sure that what we are saying is correct, or we are actually lying, then we tend to have closed body language or even hide our mouth behind our hand. Our facial expressions can show any doubt we have, and our gestures can emphasise or weaken a point. Think about the impact of shrugging while you are saying something. Paralinguistics relates to aspects of speech such as tone, volume and rhythm and they can affect the meaning of what we say. We can make something sound authentic, sarcastic or even stupid by changing the tone of our delivery.

The quality of your communication can be assessed by the response it produces and if that response is positive and the one that you wanted then you are communicating effectively. If the response or outcome is different then you will need to adapt your communication style for the person receiving it.

Listening skills

At the Supporting Champions Conference 2019 the message that came up most frequently was about listening and really listening! Listening is much harder than talking and you will find that most people prefer to talk. Listening involves more than just allowing people to talk, as to listen you need to be fully present and concentrate on what the other person is saying. If you are thinking about what you are going to say next or are developing opinions about the other person then it is likely that you are not listening fully. Sports massage therapist, Lisa Kelly, explains that listening in her role is important so that she can gain feedback about her massage, whether the pressure is too light or too hard, and then adapt to her client's needs.

Interestingly, two people I interviewed stated that while they had introverted personality types the benefit of this was that they were good listeners. Personal trainer, Ronique Redelinghuys, says that being an introvert makes her good at listening and remembering things about other people. So she can talk less and take the focus of herself she asks people questions, and as people often like to talk you can find out a lot about them which helps you to understand them and feel more comfortable with them. This can only help to develop working relationships.

Exercise physiologist, Luke Gupta, says that listening is a strength of his and this is valuable in a team environment because you won't miss things that other people in the team may miss. By listening to people it helps him to understand their concerns and then deliver an appropriate solution. He explains that people who listen can be perceived as being quiet, or not being seen as team players, and in teams it usually extraverted people that flourish. Luke does say that the drawback of listening too deeply is that you can get lost in your thoughts about what other people are saying, and then not be able to contribute when needed.

To practice becoming a better listener you need to use open questions that invite the other person to talk. Once they have finished talking you can show you have been listening by summarising the main points of what they said back to them (Supporting Champions, 2019). This can help to develop the relationship because it makes people feel like they are being heard and understood and as a result being taken seriously.

Empathy

Empathy is about understanding another's experiences and the challenges that they face. Empathy is essential because the people that you work with will have different thoughts and feelings from you, they may come from different backgrounds and have differing abilities and experiences. There can be a tendency to give people solutions based on your own preferences and experiences and expect them to enjoy them and benefit from them. This can occur in fitness training environments where we may impose the exercises that we like on other people or suggest nutritional plans that we have used and expect them to be successful.

Empathy becomes particularly important when dealing with people whose experiences that are completely different to ours. For example, Grace Kelly, says that she deals with students from inner city areas who come out to abseil and rock climb in outdoor environments that are totally alien to them. We have to understand that they may be scared or wary about doing these activities that we are comfortable with. Also, physiotherapist Laura Heathcote has had to develop empathy to enable her to adapt her practice to treat and rehabilitate disabled athletes who may have injuries that she has not had to manage before.

Empathy can be developed by asking the other person questions about their thoughts and feelings and their experiences and processing their answers so that you can appreciate their fears and then come to solutions that work for them.

Judgement

Judgement is about the 'when' part of what you say, how you say it and when you say it. It is central to the success or failure of your words or actions. Saying something at the wrong time or acting inappropriately at the wrong moment can have devastating consequences. If you reread the feedback that Steve Ingham got from coaches after the 2008 Olympic Games you will start to understand the important of judgement. The person who annoyed the coach at the wrong time when the pressure was on clearly shows a lack of judgement.

Judgement is heavily reliant on emotional intelligence and being able to read situations or assess the mood of a room or environment and then deciding whether it is the right time for you to step forwards or hold back.

Emotional intelligence

Emotional intelligence has become a buzz word in working environments but has also come under criticism with some academics questioning its validity. However, the concept of emotional intelligence is useful to us when considering personal skills. Emotional intelligence refers to how we recognise, monitor and manage our own feelings as well as how we respond to other people's emotions (Kyndt and Rowell, 2012). Emotional intelligence is based on the work of Daniel Goleman (1996) and in his book *Emotional Intelligence: why it can matter more than IQ* he explains how people of moderate intelligence may achieve more in the workplace than those with higher intelligence levels. Goleman (1996) argues that this may be due to their more developed emotional intelligence which is shown in their abilities such as self-control, persistence and self-motivation. People with high levels of emotional intelligence are able to control their emotions under pressure, read and respond to other people's feelings, show empathy and most importantly, to handle relationships smoothly.

In a previous section Steve Ingham (2019) explains how performance sport can be messy and ambiguous. This is because it is played in an unpredictable and open environment. This relates well to what Goleman (1996) says about intelligence alone being poor preparation for the turmoil and changes of fortune that life throws at us. One of the attractions of sport is that it is emotional and as it is characterised by winning and losing it can be responsible for emotional highs and lows. This is very well explained by strength and conditioning coach, Will Abbott, who works for a Premiership football team:

> "Your ability to manage your emotions is very important. There are going to be bad days when the club loses games of football and there will be fantastic days when you win big football matches. It is important to not become too emotionally involved in the little things that affect you doing your job to the best of your ability, like getting into an argument or focusing on the negatives and letting that affect your performance. If you have played sport yourself, you know how emotions can affect you and it's the same if you are a member of staff. If your team loses a game it is very easy to get caught up in the emotion but it's important to see the bigger picture and focus on the long term."

Working with people who are going through emotional highs and lows will require a specific set of skills other than knowledge and intelligence.

Goleman (1996) presents evidence that people who are skilled at controlling their emotions and can read and deal with other people's emotions are at an advantage in all domains of life. Whether it is in personal and professional relationships, or when you have to be aware of the unspoken rules in politics. We could add to this when working in the complex, unpredictable world of sport. It must be pointed out that Goleman's work, while influential, has been criticised for making exaggerated claims about its relationship to job related or leadership success (Sternberg, 1999) and whether it can be measured (Fiori and Antonakis, 2012).

When considering emotional intelligence it is important to understand the difference between reacting and responding. In an *All in the Mind* (2019) podcast, ex-professional footballer Clarke Carlisle, explains the difference. Reacting is when you act in your dominant emotion at that time which is usually anger or frustration. However, if you take the time to step back, acknowledge your feelings and reflect on your situation then you have an opportunity to respond appropriately. In effect, reacting happens immediately but responding occurs after an event when you have taken the emotion out of a situation.

Creativity/Innovation

Creativity and innovation are required when you have to formulate solutions to unfamiliar problems. Sport and physical activity manager, Vicki Galvin, explains how she often has to be innovative and 'think outside the box' to find solutions to problems. This is due to having to work with different departments who have differing agendas but are all interested in providing a better service. Physiotherapist, Laura Heathcote, finds that she has to be creative to find solutions when presented with injuries in her disabled athletes. She says:

> Being creative is really crucial because for us it is about thinking about that athlete in front of you and how you might rehab them. We might see the same injury, but it is in two athletes with different disabilities and they will present completely differently. The best rehab exercises for us are not written in a book or found online. Sometimes they may not be able to get in a certain position or do an exercise so the ability to be creative and come up with individual solutions is crucial. Also, athletes get bored if you give them the same exercises all the time. They challenge us as much as we challenge them to be creative.

A person who lacks creativity will end up applying the same solution to different problems and find that their success is limited. Once again intelligence and creativity are not necessarily linked. De Bono (2006) argues that intelligence limits creativity because an intelligent person will come up with one solution and then be able to defend it because they are good at arguing and reasoning. Creativity relies on being able to develop a range of potential solutions and then decide which one is best (Cottrell, 2015). Creativity takes time and it can be stifled by the process of sitting down and having to come up with ideas, as can happen in meetings. Anxiety and stress are barriers to creativity, but the brain does become creative when it is stimulated and engaged (Cottrell, 2015).

Adaptability

Adaptability is a skill that was mentioned by nearly all the people I interviewed. We have already talked about being adaptable in the way that you communicate to get the outcomes you want but we need to be adaptable in all situations. Personal trainer, Richard Marfell explains how he has to adapt to the restrictions of home training. He is restricted by the amount of equipment he can get in his car, the type of equipment he can use (treadmills and resistance machines are not portable), the amount of space people have in their houses and the impact of travelling. He highlights some unforeseen issues that there may be, such as children and pets joining in training sessions. He takes the attitude that you need to embrace all these factors rather than resist them and adapt your training so that everyone is happy. He also makes the point that you have to gauge how your client is feeling on any one day and then respond appropriately. You can prepare the most varied, exciting programme but if they have had a bad night's sleep or a bad day then they may not be in the right mood for a training session. Personal trainer, Ronique Redelinghuys, attributes her adaptability to the number of training courses she has attended. She is able to draw on a range of exercises and techniques and select those most appropriate for the situation.

In performance sport, adaptability to changing situations is a vital skill. Sports analyst, Chris Barry, explains how he may set up his equipment, such as cameras and computers that require electrical sockets, and then be told he has to move . He says you always need to have a back-up plan but found that bribing officials with GB team pin badges works as well.

Adaptability is vital in educational environments as coach educator, Richard Horner, says that he changes his teaching every single day to meet the needs of the coaches he is training. Coaches themselves have to be adaptable to meet the needs of the people they are delivering sessions to. This is echoed by football manager, Anthony Limbrick, as he says that he learnt to be adaptable by coaching in many different environments. He has coached four-year olds, troubled teenagers, men's and women's football teams, as well as many different sports. All these sessions have made him adaptable as a coach, so nothing fazes him, such as when his session is disrupted by another coach taking some of the players out of his session.

Having experience of many different type of coaching or instructing sessions, having as many alternatives and options as you can, and of course being creative and innovative, are ways that you can ensure you are as adaptable as possible.

These are some of the key personal skills that you will need to work effectively in sport and fitness. Different authors will focus on different skills for employability. There were other themes that came out of my research, such as the importance of being resilient and being able to overcome setbacks, the ability to work as part of a team and the importance of being able to manage your time.

Ten things that you can start doing now to benefit you in your future career

It doesn't matter how old you are or what stage of your studies you are at, you need to keep working on developing your skills and knowledge so that you have the best opportunities for a meaningful and fulfilling career. The good news is that it is never too late to start this work, but the bad news is that you will have to make sacrifices to fulfil your potential. You only have a set amount of time in each day and you need to make decisions about how you use that time. You are probably aware of Michel's Marshmallow Experiment in the 1960s where he offered children the choice of having a marshmallow now or waiting for fifteen minutes and being rewarded with two marshmallows. During the 15-minute period the researcher left the room and observed the behaviour of the children. Some children ate the marshmallow immediately, some tried to distract themselves by playing games but gave in and ate the marshmallow, but some were able to resist for the full 15-minute period.

The interesting part of the experiment came years later, as the researchers found that those children who delayed gratification by fifteen minutes were more successful in a range of life measures. They ended up achieving higher academic grades, having lower levels of substance abuse, fewer problems with stress, lower incidences of obesity and better social skills (Michel et al, 1972). The conclusion of the study was that the ability to delay gratification or make sacrifices is critical to success in life. Jordan B. Petersen (2018) in his book *12 Rules for Life* says that adapting to the discipline of medical school can fatally interfere with the lifestyle of a hardcore undergraduate party animal. But the outcome of the sacrifice made to the social life of a student is that in the future they will reap the financial benefits. Unfortunately sacrifices are necessary to improve the future. The sacrifice may be spending less time watching box sets or playing computer games and studying more, not finishing your training session early so you can get to the student union bar or spending the weekend volunteering at a local football team rather than spending time with friends or family. While it is important that you enjoy yourself and spend time socialising it is important to get the balance right between living for now and planning for the future.

Here are 10 things that you need you think about and start to work on to make you more employable and likely to secure a job or in the future. These 10 pieces of advice are gained from the 20 interviews I have conducted, the reading I have done around the subject and my own personal experiences.

1. Get as much experience as you can from wherever you can

This will come as no surprise to you having read the 20 interviews where virtually everyone emphasised the importance of getting experience. There can be a tendency for students to focus on their studies and then worry about getting the experience later. While this is an option it may not be the best plan. Alistair Bruce-Ball talked about wanting to do a post-graduate degree in journalism but being in a position where he had shown no commitment to getting into journalism at all. As a result he spent a year covering non-league football and county cricket to gain that experience. Experience is even important when you apply for some degrees let alone get a job.

Here's the thing – in order to get a job you have to show the employer that you can do the job. The only way you can do that is by showing them that you have done it before. However, if you have spent the previous three years studying you can only show that you have the knowledge needed and that there is a possibility that you may not be able to apply that knowledge in a real-life situation.

There is a conundrum here in that you need experience to get a job but how you can you get experience if you don't have a job?

There are plenty of ways for you to get the experience that you will need. Firstly, make sure that you take any opportunities you can for work experience, industrial placements and internships. Some people complain that these are unpaid, but they will offer you something more important than money and that is the opportunity to learn and put your knowledge and skills into action. Will Abbott tells us that experience doesn't need to be in elite sport, even if that is where you want to work, as when working with different groups you can learn about how to adapt your communication style and the challenges different people can pose. Internships are a rich experience where you will be expected to be part of the team and contribute accordingly. As mentioned before some occupations can be difficult to get experience in; for example, you won't be able to work as a physiotherapist, but you could volunteer at a local hospital and support the work of a physiotherapist. You may end up observing the physiotherapist for large parts of the day but by being in that environment you will see how they work and importantly consider if it is the type of work you would like to do.

The advice that Steve Ingham gives is to get involved in a local sports club and go and help out. This may be setting out equipment, setting up the hurdles or putting lane ropes in place, helping with stopwatch timings or handing out drinks. If you are helping the coach you can ask them about the session they are coaching, why they are doing that session and how they deliver the content to their athletes. The more time you spend with a team then the more trust you will gain, and you may be able to share some of the knowledge you have gained during your studies and actually start to influence people.

Another way to gain experience is to work part time alongside your studies. You can do short courses to become qualified as a lifeguard, fitness trainer, trampolining coach and then work in a gym or sports centre in your spare time. After school sports clubs and children's sporting holidays are a great way to learn about coaching, teaching and working with children. You will need some coaching awards and a willingness to try out new things. In this type of work you will be sharing your knowledge and learning how to work with people as well as earning some money.

Experience can come in different ways. For example, Emma Ross talks about a colleague who set up a dog walking business and while it may not look relevant it helped them to develop skills that can be transferred to other environments. As well as being able to listen and communicate effectively you will have to be adaptable and develop the trust of the dog owners as taking dogs for a walk can be treacherous due to the presence of other dogs, irresponsible owners and traffic hazards.

2. Learn from your experiences by reflecting on them and recording them

Experience is invaluable but only if you can learn from it. Again it sounds obvious but I'm sure we all know people who keep making the same mistakes over and over again as they don't learn from their past experiences. Work experience can be seen by students as not being important, or of any value as they feel they are being taken advantage of or made to do the menial jobs, like cleaning the gym equipment. While some aspects of work experience may seem trivial, you have to find opportunities to learn and put yourself forward to do things and talk to people during that time.

Experience has limited value unless you are able to reflect on it, assess your strengths and weaknesses and then start to work on your weaker areas. There are several frameworks and ways of reflecting and you may find that these work for you, but some people find them off putting and complicated. Reflection can be done simply by asking yourself reflective questions. For example, after delivering a coaching session or an exercise session you may ask:

> What did I do well?
> What did I do poorly?
> How can I improve for next time?

When considering what you did well or poorly you can look at specific aspects of your performance. Ghaye and Lillyman (2006) suggested that there are five key aspects to good performance – communication, decision-making, teamwork, observation and judgement. You can assess how well you have done in each of these categories and possibly add in some of the skills explored earlier, such as listening, adaptability and creativity. Often it is easier to focus on two or three aspects of your performance and you can change these weekly or from session to session.

It is really important to record your answers to these reflective questions so that you have a record of how you have progressed over time. Once you have completed a session and asked yourself what you can do to improve it is good practice to set out two or three actions that you will implement next time. For example, in a coaching session the children may not have all have done what you asked them to do because you didn't communicate what you wanted effectively, so you need to be clearer or communicate differently next time. The children may have got bored and become unruly, so you may need to have more variety or engage different children in different ways.

In this way you will start to develop your skills and experiment with different ways of doing things. All situations can be reflected on, from the smallest interaction with a customer when you hand them a towel, to what you said to an athlete after they had failed to win the medal that they had worked for their whole career. Everything you do, good or bad, is a learning experience if you make it one.

Engaging a friend or mentor to reflect with is a really valuable way of reflecting. They can ask you specific questions and give you a second opinion on how they thought you performed. We may have the tendency to gloss over our weaknesses and ignore them, but a friend may make us face up to the real issues and make observations about things we can't see. It is valuable to have a mentor, who is a person with more experience than you or someone working in a role that you aspire to. Performance nutritionist, Emma Gardner, stressed the importance of having a mentor who can provide advice and guidance to you about your career. A good mentor will be able to ask you questions that make you think about what you do, why you do it that way, and how you could do it differently.

Reflection is also really important when it comes to learning knowledge. Knowledge on its own has limited value and when knowledge is presented you will need to answer the question 'so what?' or 'what does this learning mean to me?' You can reflect on how you are going to use what you learn in a real-life situation. In particular if you read a journal article or book chapter you need to synthesise the content that is relevant to your work or future work out and think about how you could embed the ideas in your practice.

Learning by watching other people can be another important source of learning and as you watch another person you can take the best bits of what they do and also take out learning about what not to do. However, this vicarious learning is no substitute for actually doing something yourself. As football manager, Anthony Limbrick, points out - you can watch as many coaching sessions as you like but you've got to be able to deliver a session yourself and the amount of 'doing' has to vastly outweigh the amount of 'watching'. To get the most out of observing other people you can answer these questions:

What was interesting to me as I watched this coach?

What did the coach do that I could use (or avoid doing) as a practitioner?

Using these types of question you can focus on the best of their practice and consider how you could model your behaviour on theirs.

Although it may be time consuming it is good practice to keep a diary or journal of your reflective work. It acts as a record of your development as a practitioner in sport or fitness and can be useful to look back on when things aren't going so well. It is also a useful source of information when you go for a job interview. One of the questions commonly asked is about giving examples of how you have changed your practice in response to something not going well and you will have evidence of this. You may be asked how you think your skills have developed over time and you will be able to give concrete examples of what you have done to develop your skills and what the impact has been on your practice. Finally, it is a way of making sure that your experience in the workplace counts and that you can maximise your learning from it.

3.   Be clear about your goals but be prepared to review them regularly

At the start of this book I said that it is important to have a clear goal for your career so that you can make sound decisions on what you should be doing and avoid being an aimless student. While it is important to have a goal, it is also important to make sure that you review your long-term goals regularly so that you can continue on the right course in your life by adapting your short-term goals. A useful analogy here is that when an airplane takes off the pilot sets the destination for the plane and decides on the route they will follow to get there. This information is entered into a computer and the airplane follows the stored flight plan. However, during the journey the plane may be blown off course by wind, its progress may be hampered by rain or it may be heading towards a storm. As a result the pilot has to make small or large adjustments to the flight path to account for these unforeseen events and ensure that the passengers are safely delivered to their destination. On rare occasions the airplane has to land somewhere else for safety or practical reasons. You may find that the path that you originally chose is working well and you reach your destination without incident or you may find that you have to adjust your goal or your route towards the goal due to things that happen during the journey.

The goals we set ourselves need to be subject to constant review and adaptation based on the experiences we have and the knowledge we gain. Your goals as an 18-, 30- or 50-year old will be different as you change and the circumstances of your life change. Some people undergo massive career changes, such as Richard Marfell, who went from working in design to becoming a personal trainer. It would be foolish to keep working towards a goal that was no longer relevant. As an 18-year old I made it my goal to retire aged 50 but when I got to 50 I realised that I was enjoying what I was doing and had no desire to replace it with something else that I would potentially enjoy less. My 18-year old self had no idea what I would be doing or be like aged 50, and it would have been crazy to hold myself to that goal.

This is another reason why work experience is so important because it is that feasible you could study for three or four years and get the job you thought you wanted only to find out you don't enjoy it, or it doesn't suit your personality. I'm not saying you should constantly change your work-related goals, but little adjustments of your radar are always going to be beneficial.

Please do set yourself goals but don't be afraid to constantly review these goals and take the action necessary to alter direction as you grow as a person and develop your skills.

4. Gain as much knowledge as you can about as many disciplines within sports science as you can

The advice I gave you early on about knowing what to do and focusing your studies on that goal does have a potential drawback. The drawback is that you may focus on one subject at the expense of others. One of the great things about studying sports science is that it has many, varied disciplines within it. You get to study some hard science such as anatomy and physiology which has elements of human biology and chemistry; biomechanics which has combines biology and physics, and sport psychology which is a branch of science that studies human behaviour. However, you also get to study subjects such as sports sociology about the role of sport in society and that often includes the history of sport. You get the chance to understand the disciplines of coaching, instructing and teaching and you learn how to coach or instruct strength and conditioning techniques.

Sports science is a multidisciplinary subject and while you may focus on one discipline you will benefit from knowing as much as you can about the other ones. For example, if you are coaching someone you need to know about the skills of coaching and have a knowledge of training techniques within that sport. But the athlete may also need advice on what they should be eating, how they should be recovering and what they can do to control their anxiety before a big competition.

To meet the needs of someone you are working with you need to know as much as you can, and you have two choices. Either, you can answer their questions by saying 'I'll get back to you on that one', or you can answer their question there and then because you have read and studied so broadly that you are prepared for as many questions as possible. The time to do this reading is when you are studying because you have the resources and support that you need around you. You have also the crucial commodity of time, if you choose to spend it this way, and sacrifice time that you may use socialising or watching television.

Another reason why studying broadly is important is that you may work as one part of a multidisciplinary team and if you have only specialised in one area you may not understand what the sports analyst, nutritionist or physiotherapist is saying. This limits how much you can contribute to the team and it may affect your credibility with the rest of the team members.

So read journal articles, read textbooks, study respected websites, listen to sports related podcasts and watch programmes that will contribute to your learning. Write down what you learn and consider how you could use the knowledge in practice. Take in as much knowledge as you can while you have the time and the opportunity.

5. Have as many sport-related experiences as you can

Previously I explored the importance of having empathy and putting yourself in another person's shoes. It can be difficult to have empathy fully when you haven't actually had the experience yourself. Linford Christie, the Olympic 100m Gold medallist from 1992, once said that anyone who had not been in the same situation as he had would not have anything worthwhile to say to him. This is because they could never understand what it was truly like to be in the starting blocks for the final of a 100m race at the Olympic Games.

He may have a point, so we have to ensure that we have come as close as we can to these experiences. It is very likely that as a student of sports science that you have performed at a high level in your sport and understand the discipline needed to adhere to a packed training schedule. You have probably experienced the pain of DOMS and what it is like to be completely exhausted and barely able to get out of bed the day after a heavy training session. You may also be able to appreciate some of the psychological pressures that athletes can find themselves under and the stress and anxiety created by competition, particularly when a large audience or crowd is involved.

These sporting experiences can help to develop a certain amount of empathy, but you will really have to listen to the experiences of athletes to get a real feel for what they are going through. Also, while you are studying it is essential to try out as many sports as you can and experience the training techniques and fitness tests that you may ask people to do. Grace Kelly talked about when you are teaching outdoor pursuits you have to have experienced all the activities that you are instructing yourself so that you can have the emotions that people doing them for the first time will have. You need to be able to remember what was like the first time that you abseiled, rock climbed or went exploring in dark caves.

Luckily, during your studies opportunities will arise when you can experiment with different things. For example, when you study sports nutrition you will learn about carbohydrate loading, high protein or high fat diets, sports supplements and sports drinks. You can try these out to see how you feel and how much energy you have. In sport psychology you will learn about psychological interventions such as imagery, progressive muscular relaxation, breathing control and techniques to increase arousal levels. You need to experience these and understand what the effects they produce and when they may be beneficial to recommend to someone.

You can try out as many fitness training and strength and conditioning techniques as you can, so you know what they feel like and the benefits they bring. Experiment with training for strength, hypertrophy, muscular endurance; try out Olympic lifts, supersets, pre-exhaust training and plyometric training. Have a go at interval training, HIIT sessions and tempo training. Do as many fitness tests as you can so you know what exhaustion feels like in the multistage fitness test, VO^2 max test or the Wingate test. If you can, experience training in environmental chambers that simulate extremely hot and extremely cold climates. The more experiences you can have the better placed you will be to use these methods and understand exactly what they are like to go through and the pain that they bring. Also, you can honestly say 'I would never ask you to do something I haven't done myself'.

6. Be a teacher and find opportunities to share and apply your knowledge

Another way to gain experience and build your confidence is to teach or support other people. You have to remember that most people who are involved in playing sport or going to the gym have a very sketchy knowledge of what they are doing and why. Also sport and fitness are areas where there are a lot fallacies or misunderstandings about what people should be doing. An easy way to share your knowledge is to talk to people about their training or their nutrition and let them know that you are studying sports science. It is likely they will start asking you questions about training techniques, nutritional strategies or how they should recover. In these situations it is important that you are seen to be sharing your knowledge rather than preaching to them or being a know-it-all.

You can also share your knowledge by helping out a friend or family member who is training for an event such as the London to Brighton Bike Ride or they may have started going to the gym to achieve a certain goal. You can offer your services if they need advice on any aspect of their training or preparation. You may be able to support them throughout the whole process and even go training with them and introduce new types of training sessions to them. You can then blog about what you have been doing or get them to blog about their progress and make posts on social media. You may find that other people will ask for your advice and before long you will have developed a consultancy service.

This type of support does demand a commitment of time and effort on your part but again you will learn so much from the experience. It also closely mimics they type of work you may do in the future and gives you a chance to develop the skills you need to work with another person.

7. Develop as wide a skills set as you can

It is important to become as well qualified as you can whilst you study. There are two reasons for this. Firstly, it increases your chances of employability and of fitting the criteria of a job description. Secondly, it means that you will have more options when it comes to working with other people. A good example of this was presented by Ronique Redelinghuys who has a sports science related degree (Biokinetics) but she also has qualifications in sports massage, Pilates and yoga. As a personal trainer she can be adaptable and deal with each person in a different way. She is able to treat any sports injuries or movement issues affecting a person before they start working on their fitness. She can teach also Pilates and yoga classes and incorporate these techniques into a personal training session if she needs to. Having this range of skills must have played an important role when she secured her job on Necker Island, as she offers skills that are often covered by two or three people.

In terms of employability, if you attend an interview and the selection process comes down to a decision between you and another person then it is likely that the person who has the most skills to offer will get the job. Having a wide skills set also means that you have variety in your working role rather than doing the same thing every day. Personal trainers often offer exercise to large groups through circuit training or yoga and this gives them a chance to show their skills and promote their 1:1 services in personal training or sports massage.

8. Practice your communication skills as often as you

Communication comes in verbal and non-verbal forms and is always seen as one of the most important employability skills. Learning to communicate well is a lifelong process but while you study you can create opportunities where you have to communicate. This can mean taking yourself outside your comfort zone and into situations where you may not want to be. Doing presentations to a group is one way that you can develop your communication skills.

When I was an undergraduate I had a good friend who hated presentations. In his first year he did a presentation where he shuffled into class looking scruffy, with a black plastic sack to carry his books and did a presentation where he spent the whole time looking down at his notes and not looking at this audience once. However, by the third year he had become the best presenter in the group. He spoke without notes, supported his words with slides of relevant pictures and engaged the whole group through eye contact and body language. He is now a successful schoolteacher. In the intervening years he had embraced the presentation process and learnt how to communicate and engage with a group.

As well as presentations, working in groups and delivering coaching or training sessions are excellent opportunities to try out your communication skills. You need to embrace these opportunities to communicate and importantly you need to reflect on your performance and get as much feedback as you can to enable you to improve.

9. Develop contacts and a professional network

According to BASES (2010) 45% of employment is gained through a person's contacts or making speculative approaches to employers. This tells us that making contacts and having a professional network is vital. Contacts can be developed during periods of work placements or internships as well as through attending conferences and making the most of the people you meet when you are studying.

Developing a network takes a bit of effort as you will need to stay in touch with people or engage with them through social media. There are websites, such as LinkedIn which facilitate the process of developing a professional network as well as being a site where job vacancies are posted. Instagram and Facebook can also be used for this purpose, but they do tend to be more about personal friends than professional networks, although there are some professional groups that you can join. Becoming a member of British Association of Sport and Exercise Sciences (BASES) is also an important step to take as it is recognised as the professional body for sport and exercise sciences in the UK.

10. Make the most of the opportunities and the luck that comes along the way

During your studies and your career you will have opportunities to do things that can enhance your employability skills. For example, internships or work experience may seem time consuming or inconvenient but it is worth putting yourself out for them. They will offer you chances to develop your skills and nurture contacts in the industry. You can make opportunities for yourself as well by contacting influential people or offering your services to people who you think might need them. Opportunities won't be lost they will be taken up by someone else who will gain the benefits that could have been yours.

Planning and creating opportunities are essential to your career but don't underestimate the role that luck plays. Our careers are the result of the opportunities given to us, those we make for ourselves and the things that happen by luck, although often luck we have created for ourselves. Sports journalist, Adam Leitch , talked about being taken on by a newsroom and being sent off to do a six-month training course and when he came back all the other journalists had left. He was the senior journalist aged 21. I have had luck in my career, such as seeing a job advertised in the newspaper I had used to protect the floor while I painted the changing rooms in my first job. That job changed the course of my life at the time. Some people would dispute that lucks exists, but this was well illustrated when golfer Gary Player said, 'the harder I work the luckier I get'.

Final thoughts

This list of ten important things you can do is not exhaustive and it's fair to say that if you can do all these ten things you are going to be very busy! But the more of these ten things that you do will ensure that you have made the most of your experience of studying and you will be in a position to reap the benefits of the sacrifices you have made.

Gaining as much knowledge as you can get, getting experience and developing personal skills are all central to your chances of a successful career. But there are other variables as well. I spoke to Joe Brittingham, a baseball and soccer coach in America, and in his work he stresses the importance of three personality variables or ACE principles – attitude, concentration and effort. These are variables that are entirely under our control at any time that have a huge impact on how we perform and how we are perceived by other people. The importance of a positive attitude to work and towards other people cannot be reinforced enough, as it affects how other people see you and whether you are seen as being easy or difficult to work with.

References

All in the Mind (2019) 'A tale of recovery from Clarke Carlisle and his wife', *BBC Radio 4*. [Podcast] 24th April 2019. Available at: https://www.bbc.co.uk/programmes/m0004f2q (Accessed 30th April 2019).

Cottrell, S. (2015) *Skills for Success: Personal Development and Employability*. London, Palgrave.

BASES (2010) 'A Guide to Careers in Sport and Exercise Sciences'. Available at: https://www.bases.org.uk/imgs/a_guide_to_careers_in_sport_and_exercise_science_non_members801.pdf (Accessed 25th May 2015)

De Bono, E. (2006) *Teach Yourself to Think*. London, Penguin.

Fiori, M. and Antonakis, J. (2012) 'Selective attention to emotional stimuli: what IQ and openness do, and emotional intelligence does not', *Intelligence*, vol. 40, no. 3, pp. 245–54.

Ghaye, T. and Lillyman, S. (2006) *Reflection and Writing a Reflective Account*. Maisemore: The Institute of Reflective Practice – UK.

Goleman, D. P. (1995) *Emotional Intelligence: Why It Can Matter More Than IQ for Character, Health and Lifelong Achievement*, New York, Bantam Books.

Ingham, S. (2019) 'Steve Ingham on developing performance people', *Supporting Champions* [Podcast]. 24th April 2019. Available at: https://www.supportingchampions.co.uk/ (Accessed 25th April 2019).

Kyndt, T. and Rowell S. (2012) *Achieving Excellence in High Performance Sport.* London, Bloomsbury

McEwan, I. (2019) *Machines Like Me.* London, Jonathan Cape.

Mischel, W., Ebbesen, E.B., and Zeiss, A.R. (1972) 'Cognitive and attentional mechanisms in delay of gratification', Journal of Personal Social Psychology, vol. 21, no.2, pp.204-218.

Peterson, J.B. (2018) *12 Rules for Life: an antidote to chaos.* London, Allen Lane.

Sternberg, R. J. (1999) 'Review of Daniel Goleman's Working with Emotional Intelligence', *Personnel Psychology*, vol. 52, no. 3, pp. 780–3.

Supporting Champions (2019) 'Top 10 take home messages from the Supporting Champions Conference'. Available at: https://www.supportingchampions.co.uk/ (Accessed 20th April 2019).

Chapter 4 – What you need to do to land the job

Introduction

Once you have finished your studies and gained the skills and experience you need you are at the point where you will be applying for jobs. While this may not be the most glamorous part of the process it is certainly the most important. All the time and effort that you have put into your education could be wasted if you don't become adept and clever about applying for jobs. Some people can find it difficult to present the best version of themselves on paper and may rely on their personal skills to get them the job they want. But you won't get to the point of an interview if you haven't mastered the basics of the application process.

You may recall the statistics that there are around 15,000 graduates a year from sports science degrees and there are a very limited number of sports science related jobs for that cohort of graduates. There will be significant numbers of graduates looking at the same websites as you and then applying for the same jobs. For example, football coach Richard Horner identifies that there are around 150 applicants for each football academy job that comes up. So, it is likely that for each job advertised there will be over 100 applicants and the employer will be looking for a shortlist of around six applicants to interview. This tells you that the odds that stacked against you even getting an interview so you have to ensure that your application lands with the most impact. The process of applying for jobs can be time consuming and disheartening and it is important to be resilient and keep learning in response to feedback you have received.

In this chapter we will look at how employers recruit people from the job advertisement to the interview and the resources that you will need to prepare during this process. You have a choice with job applications of either just doing enough, cruising through and hoping that an employer will like you or you can give it your best effort and work hard on each application.

Understanding job advertisements

You are probably attracted to a job advertisement due to the job title or by the employer who is offering the position but to decide whether it is worth applying for you will need to read more deeply. The two key sections on a job advertisement are the job description and the person specification. You have to read the job description to see if the work is what you like to do and whether the terms and conditions will suit you. The person specification is a list of qualities and attributes that the employer needs or would like in a person they wish to employ. To get an interview you will need to match around 80-90% of the criteria on the person specification.

The job description will tell you what the duties and responsibilities of the job will be. You have to make sure that these appeal to you and give you the opportunity to use your skills and knowledge. They will need to match your level of education and experience. The job description will also tell you how you will be managed, who will be responsible for you and who you may be responsible for. It will also tell you key information about the job such as the salary, working hours, holiday entitlement and location of the work.

The person specification is about you and will be the criteria that decide whether you will be shortlisted and will also form the basis for most of the questions asked at interview. It is usually split up into essential and desirable qualities. They will be a mixture of qualifications, experience and personal skills and qualities. As identified before you will need to match most of these criteria to show that you are appropriately qualified and experienced. You may be missing or have only partially met a couple of criteria and this can be addressed by showing how you are working on them or intend to gain them in the future. If you don't fulfil most of the criteria then you have to question whether it is worth the time and effort applying for the role.

The job advertisement will usually tell you about the company that you would be working for. It will explain what is important to it, its values, and the type of company that it is. For example, the company may describe itself as 'dynamic', 'unique' or 'aspirational' or alternately as 'creative' and 'formal'. Its values may be that it is aims to support people in their sporting careers or develop as individuals. You need to be sure that the company's values match your own and you like what they do. When you apply for a job you can try and match the language of the job description to your own application. For example if the language used is dynamic and upbeat then you can present your application in a dynamic and upbeat way.

At this point it is beneficial to do some research into the company. This can be easily done by accessing the company's website or looking at their LinkedIn profile. You will need as much information as you can find out about the company when you come to interview so that you can explain why you would like to work for them but it can inform your application as well. It is useful to find out about different roles in the company, who is working there, who do they work with (athletes and coaches), how the company is funded and get an idea about its culture and values.

Some job advertisements will make an offer that you can gain further information by contacting a nominated person in the organisation. This is a good opportunity to find out more about the work but you need to be clearly focused when you talk to them and have three or four questions pre-planned to ask them. This shows the employer your enthusiasm for the role and taking the effort to build a relationship may increase the impact of your application. However, you need to be aware that the employer will also use any initial exchanges to form first impressions about you and your suitability for the role.

Applying for jobs

The job application will either be done through an application form and covering letter or a CV and covering letter. It is important that you apply with the correct resources or it is unlikely that your application will even be looked at. In reality, if an employer has 100 applications they will initially look at each CV for around 30 seconds. In that time they will look to see how closely you match the person specification and how well your skills would fit into their organisation. If they consider that you are a good fit they will put you into the group of people they may possibly interview before having a longer look to decide on the shortlist.

CVs

The CV is the key document for job applications and even if you are asked to apply using an application form you will be able to use the content of your CV to help you complete the form. It presents your education, qualifications, skills and any work-based experience that you have had. It must be done succinctly as the CV must not be longer than 2 sides of A4 paper. It is important to have a generic CV that covers all your qualifications and experience to date. You might use this one to post online at job recruitment sites. However, you will need to specifically tailor your CV to each post that you apply for. This tailored CV will show how you are suitable for a specific role and link to the role's job description and person specification. The best way of showing your suitability is by giving as much evidence as you can that you have the experience required for that job. The CV should contain the following information.

1. **Name and contact details**
Include your contact telephone number and email address. You could also provide a link to relevant work-related social media sites. You don't need to provide personal details such as your age, marital status, nationality or postal address.
2. **Short personal profile**

This should tell an employer who you are, what your interests and passions are and summarise your key skills. You might also include your career aims or goals. It should be no longer than four lines. For example, you might write ' Sports Science graduate with particular expertise in physiology and experience in supporting athletes to achieve their best performance. My goal is to work in physiological assessment and developing training programmes for performance athletes'. Although this should be edited to make it specific to each job that you apply for.

3. Education and qualification history

Put your qualifications in order of importance with the most recent ones first. If you are currently studying for a higher qualification then list that first with its intended completion date. For each qualification you should state the dates studied, the full title of the qualification, grade achieved and where you studied for the qualification. There is no need to state the modules that you studied and the individual marks that you received.

You can list your post-16 qualifications (A-levels or BTEC courses) in the same way and state the grades that you achieved. Also include your GCSEs but no need to identify the subjects, you can make a statement saying '8 GCSEs grades A – C, including English and Maths'.

4. Career history and work experience

Again put the most recent roles first. For each role show the name of employer, dates employed, job title, main responsibilities and any achievements. Avoid putting in work that has no relevance to the job you are applying for. In this section use the pronoun 'I' rather than 'we' to make your own contribution to any achievements clear. If you have not had any previous employment then you can put in periods of relevant work experience or part-time work.

5. Skills and competencies

This is where you can explain to employers the transferable skills that you have developed. This may be while you studied or during work and work placements. These skills may be team work, self-management, adaptability, communication, project management. Again, match these skills to those required on the person specification.

6. Additional training and skills

This is where you can showcase your breadth of interest and experience and the personal experiences you have had in your life. For example, completing the Duke of Edinburgh award, any projects you have set up, coaching and fitness training awards. It is always good to show your level of IT literacy as well and which packages you can use competently.

7. Interests and pastimes

You can illustrate here that you are a well-rounded person and an interviewer may pick up on some shared interests. It is best to avoid saying things like socialising, travel and reading. Unless you have travelled to places outside of holidays or read books that may be of interest to an employer. It is good to identify the sports or activities you are involved in and any particular achievements.

8. References

You will need to supply two references to an employer and you should have asked at least three people if they will act as reference for you. You can then choose the two most suitable references for a position. One academic and one work-related reference is preferable. It is debatable whether you should name the references on your CV and most advice seems to say that you should put 'references available on request' as an employer will ask you for them if they are interested. It usually comes down to how much space you have and if there is space it is worth giving their names, positions and contact details. This is particularly the case if they are a person who may be known to the employer or is well regarded in their line of work.

Of course you should make sure that your CV is free from typos, spelling and grammatical errors. It is good practice to have it checked by someone who has experience of writing or looking at CVs.

Application forms

All application forms will be different but they cover roughly the same content as a CV. Most forms will be online and you need to check any guidance that is given for filling out the form and whether there are word limits for each section. It is useful to type your responses in a word document and then cut and paste your words into the online document. This means that spellcheck is used and also if the website crashes you still have a copy of your work. When filling out the application form it is important that you do three things:

1. Show how you fit the person specification

The person specification will list the qualifications, skills, experience and personal qualities that you need for the job so you can address each of the points on the specification in turn. Use each of the criteria as headings and write a short paragraph showing how you meet that criteria and give at least one example. When talking about skills and experience it is essential to give examples and as well as explaining the example you need to highlight your own contribution, or what you did, and what the outcome was.

2. Why you want the job

This can be based on your personal interests, your education and the experiences that you have had. Again using examples works well and you should avoid emotive statements like 'all my life I've always wanted to be a personal trainer' or 'this is the only job I've ever wanted'. In particular you should focus on what the job will do for other people and how you can support and help them rather than what the job will do for you. By all means mention what it will bring you but an employer wants to know what it will bring them.

3. Why you want to work for that particular employer

Having researched the company you should be able to put a strong case together for why you would like to work for them. It could be because of what they do, what they have achieved, the working culture that they create, or the work may align to your values and may give you the opportunities you want to learn and develop. Again it is best to focus on the company and how you would fit in with them rather than focusing on what it will bring you. It is a mistake to talk about salary and rewards unless you are going for a sales job where it is important.

Covering letters

As well as supplying a CV or completing an application form you may be asked to produce a covering letter. This should be thought of as a highlights reel or a way of drawing out the most important information from your CV or application form. It usually consists of four paragraphs on one side of A4. It should be formal and business-like in style and follow the format of a letter. You will have your address on the right-hand side and the employer's name and address on the left-hand side starting one line below your address. Below the employer's address you will put today's date if. It should be addressed to a specific person as shown on the job advertisement or to Sir/Madam if no name is available. It is worthwhile making an effort to find out a name to write the letter to as it personalises the correspondence. Whatever you do make sure that you spell their name correctly as it shows a lack of attention to detail and immediately annoys them. I can say this as someone who consistently has their name spelt wrong.

Paragraph 1 – Introduction

This paragraph explains who you are, what you are currently doing (studying or working), and what your interests and career goals are. It is similar to the personal profile on the CV.

Paragraph 2 – Why you want to work in this role and for this company

You will need to show why you are interested in this type of work and developing a career in this field. This is best done by relating it to your own experiences and giving specific examples. Also, you can show that you have researched the company by explaining why you want to work for them rather than their competitors.

Paragraph 3 – Why you are the best person for the job

This needs to be crisp and punchy and grab the attention of the person reading it. This will explain how your qualifications and experience make you the best person for the job. You need to give hard examples how your experience and skills match those in the person specification and what you can offer the company. In this section you need to convince the employer that you can do the job and you can do this by showing that you have done it, or something similar, before. These examples may have been during your studies or work placements.

There is no need to go into depth about your qualifications because it is likely that most applicants will have the same qualifications, although if you have done any relevant research this may contribute to your application. You need to show how your skills and/or experience make you stand out.

Paragraph 4 – Concluding remarks

Finish off with a sentence that shows your enthusiasm and passion and reiterate what you can offer and what the job will bring you. Let them know you are available for an interview and you would like to explore the opportunity further.

The sign off with 'Yours sincerely' if you have used their name at the beginning or 'Yours faithfully' if you have used Sir/Madam.

The interview process

The application process establishes whether you have the credentials to do the job in terms of your qualifications, experience and commitment. The interview takes this process one step further and gives the employer the opportunity to make an assessment as to whether you are someone they would like to work with and have in their organisation. They can assess whether you will fit into the culture of the organisation and the extent to which you share their values. Through the application process around six candidates will be identified and you will all be asked the same set of questions at interview. Questions will be based on the job description and person specification.

What questions will you be asked?

Most interviews start with two types of questions. Firstly, you may be asked to give a summary of yourself, and secondly about why you want the role and specifically at that organisation. This is a reiteration of what you have said on your application materials and it gives you the chance to expand on this and show your passion for the role and the company while presenting what is best about you.

The questions that follow should all relate to the job description and person specification. You need to prepare for this with evidence of how you meet each one. This is done by giving examples from your past experiences and a useful acronym to structure your response is CAR which stands for context, action, result. When giving an example you can explain the situation you were in and what you were asked to do, the actions you took and what was the outcome of these actions. For example, you may be asked to explain when you had to lead a group and any problems that you faced.

Context – when I was on a work placement I was asked to take the circuits session as the instructor was ill. This was with a group of beginners who had low fitness levels.

Action – I worked hard to establish rapport with the group by asking them questions about themselves and telling them how I was going to work with them. I got them to practice the exercises but found that one or two were struggling to get the right technique. I addressed this by demonstrating exercises again and using humour to prevent any embarrassment. During the session I was firm but fair with the group to ensure their safety.

Result – After the session the group thanked me for my instruction and asked if I would be instructing them again in the future.

What questions should you ask?

Asking questions shows that you are fully engaged with the process and need to know that the organisation suits you and meets your career needs and aspirations. It also indicates that you have spent time researching the company. Not asking questions, or asking weak questions, might indicate a lack of commitment to the position; in particular if you ask questions that were clearly answered in the job advertisement. Ask two or three questions as any more will make the interview run over time and it can look like you are trying too hard. Here are some examples of good questions to ask:

I've read the job description but what will success look like for me in this role?

I've read about the organisation's aims and objectives - what are the goals that I would be working towards?

I am focused on my learning and development over the next few years – what opportunities will I have for personal development and CPD?

I can see how I will be line manged in this role but how else will I be supported in my work?

I am at the stage where I want my career to move forwards – what are the opportunities for more responsibility and promotion in the future?

It is best not to ask about salary at this point as it can make it look like you are most interested in the money. This negotiation can come once you have been offered a position and as they want you to work for them you will be in a much better position to negotiate the salary. Also, don't ask when you will hear whether you have been successful, as it is likely that they will cover that at the end of the interview

What else might you be asked to do at interview?

Coach or instruct

There are often additional tasks that you have to do at interview. Paul Weighton, who is Regional Director at Nuffield Health, explained to me that he always get interviewees for personal training jobs into the gym and asks them to instruct three exercises. This gives him the opportunity to assess their knowledge of training techniques and instructional skills. Then he will tell them go into the gym for twenty minutes and talk to as many members as they can. He will observe how they approach people and once they have finished he asks them what they have found out. This tells Paul a lot about the interviewee's interpersonal skills and how they are likely to interact with the members of the gym. Football manager, Anthony Limbrick, explained how when he was interviewed at Southampton Football Club it was the coaching session that he presented that clinched the job for him. This is because although he didn't have the playing background that other candidates had the director of football could see that he had the required skills to deliver effective coaching sessions.

Make a presentation

Presentations are a common form of assessment in interviews as it gives the employers a stronger impression of many personal skills, such as communication skills and the ability to engage with a group. It is likely that you have done many presentations during your time studying so you will be aware that you need to prepare well and practice the presentation. During the presentation you need to engage the audience with your content and by scanning the room using eye contact. Your presentation needs to be memorable so inject some originality through the use of media into the presentation. It is good to be a bit different but avoid being too quirky or acting like a comedian.

Complete group tasks

Group tasks are an opportunity to show yourself in a good light but they are fraught with danger. Group tasks are designed to see how you work with other people and sides of your personality that don't come across at a one-to-one interview. Being too dominant or too quiet are the main problems. You do need to make your voice heard but it may be best to let other people start and then find an opportunity to come in and present your own ideas or thoughts. In particular you need to be patient, tolerant and open minded. Losing your cool, being bossy or saying something controversial are guaranteed ways of being marked down in these activities.

What else should I consider?

How should you behave before and after the interview?

There is the classic story of a person going for interview and having an argument with someone in the car park only to find that they are the head of the interview panel. While this is unlikely to happen it is important to remember that you are being observed the whole time you are in the company's building. You will be judged on how you treat the all people in the organisation. That may be the caretaker who helps you with parking or the person on reception when you check in and who takes you to the interview room. It is beneficial to engage with these people and have a conversation with them. You can ask them about how they enjoy working for the company. Organisations have been known to deliberately make the interview run 20 minutes late to see how you react while you are in the waiting room. Staying calm and taking the time to talk to people is the best response to any delays.

What should you wear to the interview?

This can be a thorny issue and the best advice would be to dress smart and in a traditional manner. It is not always necessary to wear a business suit unless that is how you will be dressed in the workplace. It is best to avoid sportswear but certainly bring your training kit in case you are asked to demonstrate something practical. If you can find out in advance what you should wear from someone in the organisation that you know or have spoken to then that would be the best approach.

Final thoughts

Passion is the key to securing a job and being successful in it. In Chapter 2 several people interviewed identified that as the most important thing when working in sport, and particularly performance sport. For example, strength and conditioning coach, Will Abbott, explains that the majority of people who work in sport don't do it for the money but because they are passionate about sport. You need to be passionate because the demands placed on you can be quite extreme and you need to have the motivation to keep giving your best.

Passion is really an expression of your intrinsic motivation, what you really care about and what matters most to you. Passion is not impacted on by material or financial rewards and is seen as a powerful emotion that compels us to do something.

It is important to convey your passion for the work role during the interview process by showing how important it is to you and how much it means to you. Most people who work supporting sportspeople do so because they are passionate about sport, working in sporting environments and helping other people be successful. This can come at a cost to their social or family life but they are willing to make the sacrifices needed to support other people and achieve their own goals. Passion is important and you need to show it without appearing too keen as it can come over as being desperate.

Finally, this process needs resilience as it is often a marathon rather than a sprint. Unfortunately, there may be setbacks and you may miss out on your dream job but you need to keep going. Each interview acts as experience for you and you can learn from your performance. Working in sport can be a wonderfully fulfilling experience and I have loved the 30 years I have spent working in different sports related environments and particularly with some interesting and inspirational people.

I hope that the information in this book will support you through the process from your education into the workplace and I wish you every success and enjoyment in your chosen career.

Additional resources

Supporting Champions website

https://www.supportingchampions.co.uk

Careers in Sport website

https://careers-in-sport.co.uk/